Psychiatry and Religious Faith

ROBERT G. GASSERT, s.j.
and BERNARD H. HALL, m.d.

*Psychiatry
and
Religious Faith*

FOREWORDS BY GERALD KELLY, S.J.,
AND KARL MENNINGER, M.D.

New York · The Viking Press

IMPRIMI POTEST:

John J. Foley, S.J.
Provincial, Wisconsin Province

NIHIL OBSTAT:

John A. Schulien, S.T.D.
Censor librorum

IMPRIMATUR:

✠William E. Cousins
Archbishop of Milwaukee
February 3, 1964

First published in 1964 by The Viking Press, Inc.
625 Madison Avenue, New York, N.Y. 10022

Published simultaneously in Canada by
The Macmillan Company of Canada Limited

Library of Congress catalog card number: 64-16884
Printed in the U.S.A. by The Colonial Press Inc.

TO OUR PARENTS—
WITH AFFECTION
AND GRATITUDE

Contents

Foreword by Gerald Kelly, S. J

Shortly after the conclusion of World War II, a training program for psychiatrists was offered in Topeka, Kansas, which grew into the Menninger School of Psychiatry. From the very beginning the School offered an elective seminar dealing with the relations of religion and psychiatry as they affected the work of the psychiatrist. In this group were several Catholic physicians, and some of these came to believe that they might profit immensely from a refresher course on the fundamentals of Catholic philosophy and asceticism while pursuing their training. It was my privilege to be invited to conduct this refresher course. During an entire school year a dozen or fifteen of us met every Sunday morning for about two hours of discussion of various aspects of our faith and their relevance to psychiatric theory and practice. And on many of the Sundays, perhaps even half of them, we had afternoon informal sessions in the apartment of one of the physicians, Bernard H. Hall. My friendship with Doctor Hall had begun while he was a medical student at the University of Kansas; it was profoundly strengthened during these sessions in Topeka. Some years later, I had Father Gassert as a student, and another friendship was formed. This twofold friendship is no doubt the main reason why I was asked to write this Foreword.

But there is another reason. From the time I started teaching moral and pastoral theology I have been convinced that there should be an especially close bond between priests and psychiatrists. They both deal with the human personality under especially intimate aspects. It is seldom that a Catholic psychiatric patient can be adequately treated without the sympathetic help of a priest. This does not mean, as the authors of this book correctly point out, that the psychiatrist himself must be a Catholic, nor does it mean that the priest should be in any sense a psychiatrist. But both priest and psychiatrist should have a genuine mutual respect for and understanding of each other and their respective spheres of influence on the human person.

My work with the Catholic psychiatric residents was not limited to the one year of weekly sessions in Topeka. During the following school year the doctors kindly came to St. Mary's College, near Topeka, almost weekly for panel discussions with my theological students. The "academic" result of these meetings is difficult to appraise; it might even be negligible. But I was much more interested in what might be called the "human" result—which was not only tangible but profound. By the "human" result I mean precisely the spirit of mutual respect and understanding which I tried to describe in the previous paragraph. As the meetings at St. Mary's progressed, one could see that, despite the disagreements (of which there were many), there was a constantly increasing warmth of friendship developing between the seminarians and the psychiatrists. This is certainly the best possible foundation for mutual respect and understanding.

The present book is a good example of collaboration resulting from such mutual respect and understanding and founded upon warm friendship between priest and psychiatrist. And I might add that anyone who knows Father Gassert and Doctor Hall as I know them will readily understand that their book does not mean the sacrifice of wholesome independent judgment on the part of either. It represents what any real collaboration should mean: a distillation drawn laboriously from such discussion that started with disagreement and ended with truly judicious compromise.

Foreword by Karl Menninger, M.D.

One feature of the Menninger School of Psychiatry of which we have always been proud is its international, ecumenical, democratic composition. Faculty and student body have included representatives of over thirty nations. Some of them were Roman Catholics, some were Greek Catholics; some were Presbyterians, some were Methodists; some were Reformed Jews, some were Orthodox Jews; some were Mormons, some Moslems, some Hindus, some Buddhists. All these young men and women were attempting to understand better and thereby offer help to troubled people in the search of a better way of life. The agents employed were physical, chemical, social, and psychological; the intangible forces depended upon were love, hope, and faith.

On the basis of this philosophy it seemed appropriate to offer an elective seminar on religion and psychiatry, to which Father Kelly has referred. This gentle pastor and teacher and friend was a great support to me, the Dean, and to the Catholic and Protestant chaplains of the Veterans Administration Hospital where the seminar was first set up. Father Kelly put in many extra hours with some of the men, one of whom came to be the senior author of this book and a senior member of the staff of The Menninger Foundation. From this seminar was developed, first the Gallahue Conference series of The Menninger Foundation, and then the Danforth program on religion and psychiatry presided over by the Reverend Thomas Klink. The junior author was a Danforth-Foundation-supported theological fellow in this program and was a participant in and helpful contributor to many a clinical conference and teaching seminar in the Menninger School of Psychiatry. It is always a most pleasant and exciting occasion when his colleagues, the Jesuit seminarians of St. Mary's, come to The Menninger Foundation each year, in groups, for a week of spirited discussion and mutual learning.

From this background and experience there came to Doctor Hall and Father Gassert the realization of a need for putting in simple terms some of the things which are well known to us here but which might resolve the doubts or quiet the fears or encourage the faith of those who have not had our opportunities.

This book can be read to advantage by my fellow Presbyterians as well as by Catholics. If not its specific text in all details, at least the spirit of the book will be fully acceptable, I know, to our colleagues and friends of other denominations and other faiths. For the basis of all religion is the duty to love God and offer our help to His children—and psychiatry, too, is dedicated to the latter duty.

Introduction

Religion and psychiatry, the confessional and the couch, sin and sickness, the priest and the psychiatrist—pairings such as these undoubtedly bring forth varied reactions and raise many questions in the minds of most people. How does the one stand in relation to the other? Are they reductively the same? Are they friendly or hostile? What can one contribute to the other? These and many other questions can stimulate lively discussions in Catholic circles. But what happens when a priest and a psychiatrist try to come to grips with these questions?

A happy circumstance which brought a priest and a psychiatrist together for a year at The Menninger Foundation provided the opportunity for the collaboration on this book.* After many discussions, we saw that the questions which stimulated our initial encounters were not the basic

* The psychiatrist author is the Director of the Adult Outpatient Services of The Menninger Foundation. The priest author, as a member of the Theology Department of Marquette University, was a Theological Fellow in the Religion and Psychiatry Program at The Menninger Foundation, 1962-1963. He is now Dean of the College of Liberal Arts at Marquette University.

issues. Before any questions about psychiatry and religion could profitably be discussed, we saw the need for more of our fellow Catholics to develop an attitude toward mental illness and the mental-health professions that would be informed, concerned, and balanced. Our aim in this book is to lay the groundwork for such an attitude. Furthermore, since an aura of mystery commonly surrounds the ideas about mental illness and psychiatry, our aim is to remove some of this mystery.

Both of us could recall letters from priests, religious, or the laity appealing for help. A few examples may illustrate our guidelines in planning this book. Thus, we would hope to help people such as the nun in Iowa who wrote:

Doctor, what is the psychology of laziness? I have a very brilliant young man in one of my classes, but he is about to fail every course I teach. Maybe I'm wrong about his intelligence, but I don't think so. I am haunted by the conviction that he may well be one of the brightest students I have ever taught. But is there something wrong with me, or is it with him, and, whatever it is, why can't I help him? The other sisters tell me that he is lazy—that I should work him harder. If that's the cure for laziness, then it's not medicinal in my hands. The harder I try, the "lazier" he becomes. I feel as if I am in an arena with a child I don't understand. And there are many people booing in the bleachers—my principal, some other sisters who teach here, and especially the boy's parents.

I don't think this boy is understood by labeling him with the word "lazy," and as I write this I feel even more certain of my judgment of his intelligence level. I would like to have a psychiatrist's opinion about this boy. But I am afraid that if I suggest this my superior will tell me that sending a student to a psychiatrist does not make a better teacher. And I am certain that his parents would think I was saying their boy was crazy. What shall I do?

As the book was being written, we tried to think of superiors of religious communities who ask for help in selecting novices for their congregations. "Is there a psychological test," one mother superior asks, "that we could use? It would help so much if a consulting psychologist could tell us whether we should accept a person or not."

Are there priests, perhaps, who have received letters echoing the heartache of a young mother who wrote:

> Father, I've finally broken, and I feel so ashamed. After my operation, the return of my family responsibilities was more than I could handle. To add to my failure as a mother, I'm now forced by my weakness to seek psychiatric help. I feel like such an utter failure, and I fear for my husband and children. But please keep this in the strictest confidence; I want no one else to know I'm seeing a psychiatrist. Please pray for me.

We also had in mind letters such as the one received from a priest in El Paso:

> Doctor, I don't want to involve you in something unethical, but I simply don't know to whom I should turn at this point. One of my parishioners is in treatment with a psychiatrist. The parishioner has been asking to see me about every other day and is full of harsh criticism of the psychiatrist. I want to believe that the psychiatrist is a man of integrity and is treating the patient in keeping with the highest ethical standards of the medical profession. But from what my penitent tells me, it doesn't seem this way. Whom am I to believe? I do not wish to interfere with the treatment, but is it possible that I'm standing by and in so doing condoning something that is morally wrong?

And there was a letter that began:

> Dear Father, I've been seeing my parish priest about once a week for the last six months about the fact that I cannot

seem to keep a job. I want to see a psychiatrist, but my priest tells me that this is morally wrong. But I feel ill and I'm not certain that the priest is a physician in the sense that he can help me with my difficulties. What should I do?

The counterpart of the above was received from a Catholic woman in Indiana:

Doctor, I have been seeing a psychiatrist twice a week for the last seven months, and I can't tell whether he believes in Catholic dogma or not. I have tried to question him, but I simply can't tell. I'm terrified to continue the treatment because I am afraid I might lose my religion. Doctor, do you think I will lose my religion if I continue seeing this psychiatrist?

These few examples are typical. Others could be cited. In following these as guidelines, we have not attempted to write a how-to-do-it book which would make amateur psychiatrists of the priest in his rectory, the nun in her classroom, or the parent in the home. Nor have we attempted a clinical textbook that would enable the reader to spot a "schizophrenic" at fifty yards, and to sprinkle his conversation with such words as "paranoia," "psychopathic personality," and "obsessive-compulsive reaction." Finally, we have not tried to resolve the theoretical and speculative questions that may arise when a theologian reads Freud, or a psychiatrist delves into St. John of the Cross. Our aim rather is to interpret psychiatry and mental illness so that the reader can know more about mental illness and also know what he can reasonably expect from psychiatry as a method of treatment. Against this background we have chosen to consider a few specific topics that concern primarily the priest and the religious.

While priests and nuns were in our minds as our chief and most influential readers, we feel that this book is pertinent to the Catholic laity as well. In fact, many of the questions raised and the problems posed in this book are not peculiar to Catholics. The same questions and the same problems may be found in a variant form in any Christian, Jewish, or other religious group. Human needs and the search for their gratification know no denominational identity. We commit our effort to the widest, most catholic audience.

ACKNOWLEDGMENTS

When this book was in manuscript, it was read and critically commented upon by scores of friends and acquaintances of diverse professional and religious backgrounds. These included priests, sisters, and Protestant clergymen engaged in educational, pastoral, and medical work; a cross-section of the mental-health professions; and, last but not least, persons whose full-time vocations centered on raising their families in a hectic world.

To give individual acknowledgment to these many advance readers is a prohibitive task. Our only alternative is to express to all of them our sincere gratitude for their many helpful suggestions.

Our special thanks to Dr. Martin Mayman and Dr. Richard Siegal, who brought from their long experience as clinical psychologists the expert assistance we required for the chapter on psychological tests. The clinical conference in Chapter V was originally written for a public presentation by Miss Winifred Wheeler, Dr. Irwin Rosen, and Dr. Bernard Hall. The contribution of Miss Wheeler and Doctor Rosen to the book is a significant one.

The patience, equanimity, and skill of Mrs. Geraldine Alumbaugh were all sorely tested as she typed and retyped this book from scribbled notes, through draft after draft to its final form. We are particularly grateful to her. To our editor, Mr. Denver Lindley of Viking Press, our sincere thanks for his gentle wisdom and deft guidance of our efforts.

R.G.G.
B.H.H.

Topeka
1964

Psychiatry and Religious Faith

I

Psychiatry and Religion

Both psychiatry and religion are today enjoying an unprecedented popularity. Whatever the complex historical origins of these phenomena may be, the parallel popularity of psychiatry and religion, like parallel lines, seems destined in the minds of many people to extend onward with no possibility of a meeting point. The stereotyped images evoked by the words "psychiatry" and "religion" frequently contain facets that are antithetical. The result for many Catholics is the suspicion that psychiatry is by nature irreligious and that a religious person has no need for psychiatry.

Is one in danger of losing his religious faith if he seeks psychiatric help? Is psychiatry detrimental to one's religious life? Do the present-day religious revival and the increased popularity of psychiatry have anything in common? Is it possible that a Catholic could live his faith more effectively if he were aware of some of the present-day insights about "personality functioning"? Could religious leaders be more effective administrators of dioceses, parishes, schools, and hospitals if they were more conversant with human psychology and group dynamics? It is in the light of such questions that we want to examine the relationship of psychiatry and religion as they exist in our American culture.

The popularity of psychiatry today is unique in the history of medicine. Never before has a specialty of medicine had such widespread publicity. Nearly every issue of most national magazines includes something about psychiatry—if not an article, at least a cartoon. The cartoons are often designed to make the psychiatrist look funny, somewhat stupid, but never like a serious scientist. It is not these innocuous cartoons and jokes that concern the psychiatrist as he is continually reminded of the enormous attention presently paid to his science. If this popularization of psychiatry and psychological theories leads to improved and extended care for the mentally ill, or if it leads to man's understanding himself better, or if it helps a young couple to be better parents, then we can be glad psychiatry is popular. But the popularity of psychiatry often flirts with superficiality. And this danger does concern psychiatrists.

One small evidence of the superficial influence of psychiatry appears in our American language, which is now generously sprinkled with technical psychological terms. The fact that this jargon is wandering into popular usage is not what worries psychiatrists. They are worried about something much more serious. They are concerned that there is so little evidence that the deeper insights about man, gained from the hard work of psychiatric clinicians, have had more than a superficial effect upon life—the life of the individual, the family, our society, the family of nations. Psychiatry is a success as far as popularity is concerned. It is increasingly successful in the treatment of individuals. It does not wish to be a failure at contributing something of substance to the total family of man.

The popularity wave of psychiatry has had repercussions in the field of religious thought. Many attempts have been made, often of heroic proportions, to square every theoretical psychiatric issue with its theological counterpart. These efforts have reduced some of the barriers of communication between religion and psychiatry. Our concern in this book is not with the broader theoretical issues that remain unsolved between religion and psychiatry. Our concern is rather that so little of what has been learned about human behavior is being applied to education, to the care of the sick, to the ministry, to work, to the use of leisure, and to many other pertinent fields.

Psychiatry has added much to our knowledge of how people grow and change. During World War II psychiatrists learned a great deal about how a good leader leads.[1] * But many in responsible positions remain blind to these insights. To cite a hypothetical example: A bishop issues a letter to his diocese about a retreat for high-school students. It reads in part: "High-school students not attending Catholic schools are hereby ordered to attend a retreat to be held on Sunday at St. Mary's High School." The bishop, of course, clearly has the authority over his flock in religious matters, and he is properly concerned about the religious formation of the young. But he seriously defeated himself in this instance by being such a poor psychologist. Obviously one does not have to be clinically trained to recognize in the above statement an absence of knowledge about the psychology of adolescence. It would be a rare adolescent who is moved simply by a peremptory order. Yet adolescents are hungry for identity and for leadership, and they will re-

* Reference notes begin on page 161.

spond, through the power of identification, to the man who inspires them by his example.

One of the reasons that one of the authors became a convert to Catholicism was that a parish priest took time—not just time for the necessary catechetical instruction. During dozens of lazy hours, sparked sometimes with heated discussions, Father Michael Hoffman took time to expose his wisdom, his scholarship, his scientific curiosity, his love of books, his finding God in the beauty of nature—doing all this, but never forsaking for an instant his identity as a Catholic priest. He certainly did not think of himself as a psychologist, and if he had read Freud he never mentioned him. But this priest, who in a small college town had over a hundred collegiate converts in the course of a few years, could well have written a textbook on the psychology of religious faith. He knew people and he knew his faith. He disliked convert classes because he felt that the individuality of a human being is far too precious to risk the use of assembly-line methods. He knew that a vibrant faith does not come easily and is not the result of mere instruction. He encouraged "doubt"—that wonderful healthy kind of questioning that leads one to seek God through an honest and responsible engagement with life.

The importance of "identification" and the power of example have long been known, but Sigmund Freud described in scientific words this tendency in man to imitate that which he admires. We know, for example, how important it is in education. In the opinion of some, teachers are often drilled in educational techniques to the neglect of an adequate awareness of their personal impact on students, an impact that transcends the content of the course or the method of teaching. Few of us can remember much of our favorite teachers' courses; but we can all remember a favorite teacher and his or her qualities which we may still aspire to imitate.

Let us return more directly to our concern that so little of the advanced knowledge of human behavior has had much more than a superficial influence on our culture. While clinical psychiatric research has opened up some new vistas in our knowledge of man, priests and nuns are often among the last to avail themselves of this knowledge. One of the reasons for this lag is a widespread notion that psychiatry is irreligious. The fact that this notion is widespread does not make it true. This notion is rooted in the original distrust between religion and science in general, and between Freud and religion in particular, but this must be seen against its historical background. By taking the longer view we should be able to see this attitude of skepticism in its proper perspective.

There are today many psychiatrists who achieve this balanced view. They recognize the distinction between religious values and the psychological distortions of those values as evidenced, for example, in some of their patients who try to use religion as a crutch. Moreover, if these psychiatrists are familiar with the philosophical thought of the nineteenth century they will recognize the rationalistic underpinnings of Freud's speculations on religion. These speculations are not the product of Freud's scientific work. As Dr. Clemens E. Benda notes, Freud's ideas on religion are "the uncritical application of rationalistic thinking to unsuitable subjects." He goes on to say:

> We are gradually coming to understand that the system of values in any culture is deeply rooted in the religious thinking of the time. This religious framework is an

autonomous creation which transcends the particular sciences and can never be understood through one single science like biology or psychology.[2]

Yet suspicion persists. If a psychiatrist today quotes Freud, some people jump to the conclusion that he must be a heathen—an unbeliever. For, after all, did not Freud say that religion is an illusion? Indeed he did. But, as Dr. Karl Menninger has pointed out, Freud did not say that religion is a delusion, but that like art and music it can be an illusion. Admittedly this is a benign interpretation of Freud, but Dr. Menninger's further observation is pointed:

> . . . Freud did not mean to say that the religious experience was negligible or that it was false, or that it was nonexistent. I think Freud did feel that certain forms developed in the name of religion are harmful. But Isaiah thought that; and Jeremiah thought that; and Micah thought that; and Hosea thought that; and Jesus thought that. The conclusion was not original with Freud. Empty forms of religion have been criticized over and over again.[3]

Psychiatrists get rather weary of always being suspected of irreligion. There are no statistics available to show that a greater or lesser number of psychiatrists get to heaven than other men. The wholesale presumptuousness implied in the cry of irreligious psychiatry should be laid aside. Psychiatrists like all other men have their religious struggles. One is reminded of a comment of Goethe:

> He who has science or art
>   Need not religious be;
> He who has neither,
>   Let him religious be.[4]

Goethe's opinion is all too true for many people; psychiatrists do not have a patent on it. Many men do find a faith in science or art and turn away from organized religion. But the scientists and artists, like all men, hunger for truth and many, indeed, find that they need something more to live by.

Science and religion are obviously not the same thing, although both have the intent of pursuing truth. Psychiatry as a medical science is neither more nor less religious than any other science. Some psychiatrists do not find a need for a personal religion; some others do. If we can bury the resistance to psychiatric insight expressed in the concern over whether psychiatry is religious or irreligious, we could move on to take a better look at what psychiatry has to contribute to man. As we complete the funereal duty of interring this bone of contention, we might remind ourselves of a conclusion made by Father Gerald Kelly, S.J., after years of work on medical-moral problems—"It turns out in the end that what is good morality is also good medicine." [5]

Against this background we should be able to answer the often-repeated question, "Does a Catholic who seeks psychiatric help run a serious risk of losing his faith?" The answer, as any psychiatrist can tell us, is quite simple: "Not if his faith amounts to anything." There is too much concern about people's losing their faith, and not enough about their finding a faith. A faith that amounts to anything is not a fragile possession. Those who are so preoccupied with fear of losing their faith might well have reason to be fearful, for this can mean that it is built of flimsy stock. A Catholic, like anyone else, should seek psychiatric help for mental illness, not as a means of shoring up a weakened faith. And if good psychiatry is consonant with good morality, we should be able to conclude that a psychiatrist as such does not stand as a threat to his patient's faith.

In this context someone is usually ready to cite an example of a person who underwent psychiatric treatment and then later left the Church. Rarely does anyone bother to ask what sort of Catholic the man was before he went to a psychiatrist. The psychiatrist could tell you that the man was a Catholic in name only, and that the religious teachings of his faith were worn casually and were not integrated into his personality. Nor do the critics of psychiatry choose to remember that there have been patients who have found a religious faith during or after their psychiatric treatment. The following is a case in point:

A particularly rebellious adolescent was referred for psychotherapy because of his repeated school failures. He was militant in his verbal criticisms of his "old-fashioned" parents and he seemed to want to avoid any behavior that would hint that he was in any way like his father. Leaving home to come for treatment gave him the needed license to stop going to Mass. Early in his treatment his verbal attacks on the Catholic Church and on his father were frequent, truculent, and so similar that it was often difficult to distinguish which one he was talking about.

As the treatment progressed the patient came to understand better the source of his rebellion. He learned that it was a smoke screen to cover his anxiety about growing up and assuming adult responsibilities as a man. His relationship with his parents dramatically improved and he regained affectionate feelings for them. Simultaneously he showed a new interest in his religion. For the first time he read a history of the Church. Later he casually mentioned to his psychotherapist that he was again attending Sunday Mass.

In this whole question of losing or finding a faith, we must distinguish psychiatry as such from the practice of psychiatrists. If a particular psychiatrist respects no religious values, his practice may well be dangerous and harmful to the faith of his patients. At the same time, it is not the task of psychiatric treatment either to build up or to tear down one's faith or religious values. "The psychiatrist," says Dr. Rudolf Allers, "even though he may be a religious man, does not have the task of preaching good tidings; but to him it is given 'to prepare the ways of the Lord and make straight his paths.' " [6]

The sad fact today, however, is this: many people are turning to psychiatry as if it had the answer to all man's problems. Its pervasive influence in the behavioral sciences, in literature, in art, in medicine—and in many other fields— may leave some people with the false impression that psychiatry pretends to have all the answers. None of its practitioners seriously thinks it has. But what further contributes to this popular impression is the fact that many people today turn to psychiatry in their quest for "something to believe in." Under the weight of life's burdens, disillusioned with a childhood faith that has remained childish, isolated from the world around them, many of the sick in mind and heart seek something "religious" in psychiatry—and they think they find it. Psychiatry becomes for them almost a way of life. In an age of the "organization man" and the "lonely crowd," such people have found something closely akin to religion, something that meets their "religious" needs—human understanding, concern, hope. After all, psychiatry does stress the individual dignity and worth of man. Perhaps it is because that dignity is so threatened in the modern world that psychiatry has become for some a substitute for religion.

Psychiatry is not meant to be a substitute for religion, nor is it a philosophy of life. This fact, of course, is true also of any other science or art. But psychiatry can be a valuable aid in freeing a person better to understand and live his religion or to engage more successfully in his quest for life's meaning. It remains the task of Catholics as public witnesses of their faith, and in their specific roles as parents, educators, nurses, pastors, and the like, to help those who are seeking for a religion or a more deeply religious and meaningful life. And the psychiatrist himself cannot be sectarian in his work with his patients; if he were, he would already be forsaking his identity as a clinician.

Some religious writers of our time are equally distressed about the hollowness of many lives that are Catholic in name only. It is the evidence of superficiality and destructive misuse of religion that concerns psychiatrists and theologians alike. Thus, Father Andrew Greeley comments on today's "religious revival," which will remain empty unless people seek an affective union with God in contemplation. He writes:

> The absence of contemplation in our country explains the more superficial weaknesses of today's religious revival. If one does not contemplate, it is rather easy to make God a kind of Assistant Vice-President in charge of Morale or Unforeseen Circumstances while never perceiving how foolish this concept is. The "Totally Other" will remain "The Man Upstairs" if no one has time to ponder his essence. Conformity can seek comfort in religion if there is no opportunity to think about some of the less quieting

notions of Christianity. One will never get disturbed about the possibility of death and damnation if one has no time to consider these realities. Finally, in the absence of prayerful thought about the meaning of God's saving love, there can simultaneously exist such contradictions as frequent Communion and racial hatred. We American Catholics have built a splendid religious edifice but have not yet started to probe the depths of that for which we have built the edifice. Until we do, our religion—for all its glitter—will still be a childish thing indeed.[7]

A more disturbing voice reaches us from a Nazi prison where Jesuit Father Alfred Delp awaited trial and eventual execution. His reflections on contemporary spiritual life will haunt the reader of his prison meditations:

> The most pious prayer can become a blasphemy if he who offers it tolerates or helps to further conditions which are fatal to mankind, which render him unacceptable to God, or weaken his spiritual, moral or religious nature.[8]

Father John L. Thomas, S.J., has recently published a scholarly study entitled *Religion and the American People.*[9] Father Thomas was dissatisfied with the assumption that there has been a revival of religion or of interest in religion in the past two decades. By conducting a sociological research study he attempted to go beyond perceptive insights or educated guesses about this revival. He investigated the actual religious beliefs of the average American adult. His report is based on interviews with 2987 American adults concerning the role that religion plays in their lives. His findings provide us with a scientific confirmation of what men such as Father Greeley and Father Delp have written. Father Thomas concludes:

> . . . I suggest that the churches in America have failed to produce a religious elite capable of making the doc-

trines of the traditional faith relevant to our complex, rapidly changing social order or to the new insights into human nature furnished by modern science. The result has been a gradual withdrawal of religious influence from increasingly extensive sectors of human activity and endeavor. The majority even of the actively affiliated faithful often fail to discover the relevance of religion in such areas, for their understanding of religious doctrine tends to remain at the Sunday School or childhood level. Yet a religious system must remain interpretively creative if it is to avoid becoming a mere cultural residue of a subsidiary institution of society. Unless this can produce an informed elite capable of providing a relatively consistent, orderly, meaningful interpretation of the total, evolving human situation experienced by its faithful, they must turn to other sources in their attempts to "make sense" of their world. Meeting this need for a religiously interpretive creativity is undoubtedly the major challenge the churches face in America today.

Father Thomas could have continued by saying that people attempting to understand life and its purpose and disillusioned with religion have often turned in our times to psychiatry, expecting to find some understanding there.

With the findings from his research analyzed, Father Thomas takes the scientist's next step—prediction. In the final paragraph of his book he makes some predictions about the churches of tomorrow:

The popularity of religion is no necessary indication of its vitality. The traditional faiths face a radical challenge in our affluent, secular society, for unless they can define the pertinent personal and social implications of the specific transcendental beliefs and values they profess, they will lose not only their identities but forfeit their claims to the attention of the sincere. The churches must not be reduced to being *comfort stations* for the worried or *morale builders* for the culture, but neither must they become pious assemblies of *moral eunuchs*. Either they continue to interpret life within a framework of values extending above civilization and outside of human history, or they will fulfill no *irreplaceable* function.

These observations are on a far vaster canvas than the scope of this book, but we have included them because we believe that there has been a much too negative view stirred up by the false issue of religion *or* psychiatry. We wish to propose that much of this overconcern about loss of faith and the tendency to perceive the psychiatrist as irreligious can be a psychological maneuver to cover up the superficiality or falseness of one's own religion—the very things that worry the religious writers we have quoted.

We are not prophets of doom. Indeed, there are countless examples today of genuine religious dedication quietly and effectively lived. Any parish priest or any sister in a school or hospital could cite vivid examples of the deep religious life of parishioners, students, or patients. Of this there is no question. With equal certitude we affirm that psychiatry can ably address itself to some of the complexities of today's problems. Psychiatry is *not* the answer to all of life's woes. But neither is it irreligious or a danger to one's faith. And psychiatry may help cut through some of the superficialities or distortions that plague many in living their faith.

Our Catholic faith provides divinely given answers to the questions man forever asks, questions which psychiatry in itself is not competent to answer, concerning the nature and destiny of man, the problem of evil, the meaning of God. Psychiatry has certainly shed light on some partial answers to those questions; the ultimate answers come from God. Each of us must do his part in meeting religious responsibilities toward those whom he influences, to help them meet God and His Truth.

The restless hunger and suffering of others are a cry to each of us. It is important that we ourselves strive for mental health and maturity if we would be God's instrument in helping others. And what we must bring to our troubled world is the Christian message of hope, amid all the tragedy and suffering around us. We cannot stand mutely by and say that there is no answer. There is an answer, not in words, but in the Word. The unfathomable mystery of our faith tells us that the tragedy of life must point to hope, not despair.

The readers of this book are, by profession of their Catholic faith, purveyors of this hope. To such readers it should be needless to point out that the ultimate destiny of man is not simply mental health. But surely a mentally healthy approach to both the light and darkness, the joy and sorrow of life, is clearly a part of the total Christian view. What we need is a sober medium between the extremes of an unexamined hostility to psychiatry and an uncritical enthusiasm.

In this first chapter, then, before beginning the information about psychiatry and mental illness, we thought it would be useful to confront the issues relating religion and psychiatry. We hope that the information contained in the remaining chapters will become integrated into our readers' Christian view of man and their apostolic work. For such an integration Pope John XXIII appealed—an integration not just of psychiatry and Christianity but of all the scientific advances of modern man. He reminded us how necessary it is "that human beings in the intimacy of their own consciences should so live and act in their temporal lives as to create a synthesis between scientific, technical, and professional elements on the one hand, and spiritual values on the other." [10]

2

The Mental-Health Problem

The synthesis for which Pope John appealed must be preceded by analysis. Our attempt at this begins by surveying the scope of the national problem of mental health. That a problem exists is obvious to psychiatrists and to all members of the mental-health professions. Occasionally other voices are raised—a priest's, a minister's, a rabbi's—to call attention to it. Too few hear them. Recently, however, the chorus was joined by one who commanded a national audience.

It was an event of unprecedented importance for the mentally ill when, on February 5, 1963, John F. Kennedy delivered to the Congress of the United States a "Message on Mental Illness and Mental Retardation." [1] Never before had a President of the United States sought to arouse all its citizens to face the necessity of better programs for meeting these problems. After noting that the nation's progress in the treatment and prevention of physical illness has had no counterpart in the field of mental illness, the President portrayed the problem that confronts the American public.

. . . mental illness and mental retardation are among our most critical health problems. They occur more frequently, affect more people, require more prolonged treatment, cause more suffering by the families of the afflicted, waste more of our human resources, and constitute more financial drain upon both the Public Treasury and the personal finances of the individual families than any other single condition.

Mr. Kennedy discussed the cost of mental illness, pointing to the fact that 1,500,000 people receive treatment every year in institutions for the mentally ill and the mentally retarded. This costs taxpayers $2,400,000,000 a year in direct costs; the indirect costs to welfare funds and in the waste of human resources are even greater. Despite this enormous cost Mr. Kennedy noted that most such patients are crowded into a chain of antiquated custodial state institutions where the average amount expended for individual patient care is a mere $4 a day.

Mr. Kennedy continued: "But the anguish suffered both by those afflicted and by their families transcends financial statistics—particularly in view of the fact that both mental illness and mental retardation strike so often in childhood, leading in most cases to a lifetime of disablement for the patient, a lifetime of hardship for his family." Speaking for the nation Mr. Kennedy said, "This situation has been tolerated far too long. It has troubled our national conscience—but only as a problem unpleasant to mention, easy to postpone, and despairing of solution."

Some fifty years ago a private citizen tried to arouse public interest in the same problem. Clifford Beers, himself a victim of mental illness which required his hospitalization, was so appalled by the inadequate treatment of the hospitalized mentally ill that he started to do something about it. In *A Mind That Found Itself* [2] he tells how he suffered, hoping his readers would be moved to corrective action about the neglect of the mentally ill. Despite repeated disappointments and frustrations, Mr. Beers finally succeeded in getting a few associates to help him found a citizens' organization called "The National Committee for Mental Hygiene." That was in 1909. Renamed "The National Association for Mental Health" in 1950, this organization comprises local and state mental health groups of interested citizens. The following statistics,[3] released by the National Association for Mental Health, further describe the breadth of the problem:

1. At least one person in every ten—nineteen million in all—has some form of mental or emotional illness (from mild to severe) that needs psychiatric treatment.
2. Mental illness is known to be an important factor in many physical illnesses, even heart disease and tuberculosis.
3. At least fifty per cent of all the millions of medical and surgical cases treated by private doctors and hospitals have mental-illness complications.
4. There are more people in hospitals with mental illness, at any one time, than with all other diseases combined, including cancer, heart disease, tuberculosis, and every other killing and crippling disease.
5. It is estimated that there are more than half a million mentally ill children in the United States classified as suffering from severe forms of mental illness. Only a very small percentage of the total is receiving any kind of psychiatric treatment.

Other sources have released further pertinent data:

6. According to the National Council on Alcoholism there are five million people suffering from severe degrees of alcoholism in the United States.[4]

7. According to the *Medicolegal Digest*[5] there are between
   eighteen thousand and twenty thousand suicides in the
   United States every year.

These statistics are compelling, but even they fail to por-
tray the total problem. They tend to emphasize the advanced
and most severe forms of mental illness, and by so doing
they unfortunately narrow our conception of the total problem. But if the public spotlight focuses our attention on the
more dramatic forms of mental illness, even this is a gain.
Only in recent history have mental disorders more commonly been seen *as illnesses*. Extreme and bizarre behavior,
often of the antisocial kind, was commonly ascribed to various causes: punishment by the gods, demonic possession,
moral turpitude, being born under the wrong signs of the
zodiac or on the wrong side of the tracks, and the like. Illness it was not.

Today, of course, it is still the extreme forms of mental
illness that make the news. And what is read in newspapers,
heard on radio, or seen on television influences the popular
conception of mental illness. How far does this influence
reach? Most of us read a morning newspaper. If the front
page looks too forbidding, we may skip it to check on our
favorite comic strip. But when we get back to the front
page, it holds grim reminders that the human family lives
with great sorrows, great tragedies, great uncertainties, great
deprivations, great inequalities. Amid the reports of spread-
ing brutality, corruption, and threatening nuclear warfare,
of calamities of nature or technology, are stories about men
and women who have exploded in acts of violence—assault,
murder, suicide. Or there are accounts of desertion of children, severe alcoholism, robberies, prostitution.

What meaning does this record of human tragedy hold for the psychiatrist? The significance to him is a further tragedy in that he believes each of the persons who commits these acts is mentally ill. Once the psychiatrist was almost alone in this belief, but times are changing. Now a teacher of moral theology, or a judge, for example, while reading the same morning newspaper, will doubtless think first of the moral or legal issues involved in these human transgressions, but, like the psychiatrist, will also wonder to what degree the offender was a sick person.

Through the educational efforts of psychiatry and allied professions, the American public is slowly coming to understand that the murderer is a sick man, the person who commits suicide is a sick man, the father who deserts his children is a sick man. "Journalistic mental illness"—the kind that makes the front page—is only the exposed fraction of the total problem.

What of the mental illnesses that never make the front page or, for that matter, any other page of the newspaper? Most mental suffering is a private affair. Who would read all the stories that could be written about the perennial sorrow of the parents of a mentally retarded child? The loneliness and sense of uselessness of many older people would not make good copy. And what editor would publish the everyday private experiences of anger, of sorrow, of disappointment? But the reader may be asking, "Are you trying to say that those ordinary emotional disturbances represent mental illness?"

One of the aims of this book is to take the reader beyond the kind of mental illness that makes the daily newspaper. A more comprehensive theory of illness will be discussed in the next chapter. But we can note here that psychiatrists and their mental-health colleagues have been forced to recognize that illness and health are not absolute states. The psychiatrist assumes that every patient strives toward health and toward more adaptive behavior. It is because the patient has temporarily failed that he has sought help. But who of us ever succeeds in achieving complete mental health? Are we not all trying constantly to be more adaptive to the stresses of daily life? The psychiatrist knows that we all vary from moment to moment, from day to day, in mentally healthy behavior. It is hard to avoid being irritable when one has a toothache, and at the end of a hard day we may have to exert particular effort to be sympathetic with another's difficulty. But more of this later.

Assuming that the reader has the broader perspective of our national mental-health program, what can be done about it? Even recognizing President Kennedy's bold challenge is fruitless unless that recognition brings definitive social action —action aimed at the prevention and treatment of mental illness. Practical Americans not only like tangible results, they like to know what is required to achieve them. What are some of the social actions required to meet Mr. Kennedy's challenge?

Certainly one of the first must be to increase the number of opportunities for people to have psychiatric treatment when they need it. This means an increased number of psychiatrists and a larger number of outpatient psychiatric clinics. Estimates differ as to the number of hospital beds that will be needed for psychiatric patients. Some large mental hospitals have been able to close some of their wards as they have been developing larger and better outpatient departments. Certainly some of our mental hospitals need renovating or need new buildings. But such needs are met by brick and mortar. Why can we not solve this problem easily and quickly? Why can we not act immediately to inform our legislators of this need and thus obtain the appropriations? If the problem were that simple, our country could respond to Mr. Kennedy's message with dispatch.

But buildings—new or old, modernized or old-fashioned—are of no use unless they are staffed by personnel who are properly trained to treat patients. And here is the problem that even our legislators cannot immediately correct. "I am going to see if I can steal some personnel," a psychiatrist commented as he was preparing to attend a national psychiatric meeting. This psychiatrist is in charge of a large hospital; he has to spend much of his time recruiting and educating professional personnel. Obviously there is no job shortage either for psychiatrists or for any others trained in the mental-health professions. Those who are recruiting new personnel are pressured to "steal" professional workers from their present jobs where they are already needed. The shortage is highlighted in the recent Surgeon General's report about nurses: "By 1970 the number of professional nurses with advanced preparation in psychiatric nursing should be more than doubled. At the same time trained psychiatric aides should increase [from the present 101,000] to about 180,000." [6] Nurse educators and psychiatrists know these needs; they also know that meeting them by 1970 is impossible. It takes a long time to acquire the necessary clinical skills for any of the mental-health professions, and in all the training programs there is a shortage of students.

The personnel problem, then, remains the biggest block to any effective program to meet the mental-health problem. Our consideration thus far has been limited to social action that could increase the number of personnel, outpatient clinics, and hospital beds. And such action is directed primarily to the objective of *treatment*.

The problem of *prevention* requires a militant national effort to correct enormous social lags—those failures of our society to create circumstances that make for healthy mental development. This involves such items as slum clearance, the provision of adequate housing, tackling the unemployment problem, reduction of prejudice toward and restriction of minority groups, improvement of schools and recreational centers—the list goes on and on. Though the Church is aware of many of these vital needs, she is sadly cognizant of the gap that so often exists between doctrine and practice. The Church recognizes that all is not well with her own educational, parochial, and apostolic efforts. The growing sociology of religion will help spotlight both its weaknesses and its strengths, and modernizing the Church's work can contribute toward preventing mental illness.[7]

The sociological dimension of mental illness must be further explored. Social evils can precipitate mental illness as surely as stagnant water can be the breeding ground for malaria. Obviously there is no simple or single solution to the social evils underlying so much mental and emotional disturbance, but there can be no beginnings of a solution if we remain unconcerned. Apathy is the enemy here. All too many of us find "peace of mind" by simply closing our eyes to the miseries around us. Dr. Karl Menninger has noted that such a withdrawal from life and its responsibilities is not unlike a kind of suicide.[8]

How many of us say, "Yes, there's a great mental-health problem in the United States"—then promptly turn on the television and forget all about it, convinced that the problem is just too big? How many of us feel that as individuals we can do nothing about it? We may even reassure ourselves that the government is taking care of that problem! And some Catholics may try smugly to dismiss the problem with—"We Catholics have the confessional, which is the same thing as psychiatry anyway; if people would just go to church there wouldn't be all this mental illness." The confessional and psychiatry are *not* the same thing. And being a member of the Catholic faith, even being a daily communicant, is not a prophylaxis or an antidote for mental illness. Such head-in-the-sand withdrawal is not going to help solve the national mental-health problem.

Recall for a moment how a national effort, both lay and professional, markedly reduced the suffering and death caused by tuberculosis. Recall that one of the most important aspects of that successful campaign was educating people to the fact that early recognition and early treatment constitute the best prevention of serious and often fatal illness. Is such an attack on mental illness, similar in scope and effort, unrealistic? There is an obvious parallel here for the mental-health program, namely, the need to teach people that early treatment of an emotional disorder means shorter and more effective treatment; to show how early treatment can usually be handled in an outpatient service and does not require psychiatric hospitalization; to demonstrate that early treatment reduces the cost dramatically; and, most important of all, to emphasize how early treatment reduces human suffering.

The focus on early treatment brings a ray of optimism into the picture. But an obvious prerequisite for such treatment is the early recognition of the need for it. Help cannot be provided unless the need is recognized.

We can better appreciate this if we consider what happens when the need is not recognized. An unattended, progressive illness is likely to develop two characteristics: first, it will become worse, and, second, it will become more entrenched and hence more resistant to therapy. Repeatedly, in the state mental hospitals this fact is painfully demonstrated. Because of the traditional stigma of mental illness, help was not sought for the afflicted until the illness was far advanced, to the point where hospitalization was the only solution. It was only a custodial solution, for in the past psychiatry had little to offer as treatment. As a result, the mental hospitals simply grew as the admission rates far exceeded discharge rates. The common reason for discharge was death. The expanding hospitals—the name was a misnomer—became huge warehouses, custodial institutions for society's misfits where, neglected and mistreated, patients had nothing to expect except release in death. Voices were raised in protest. One was that of a spirited journalist, Albert Deutsch, who exposed this tragic situation in *The Shame of the States.*[9]

A vivid example of this shame—lest we forget it—is found in a news story published in the *Topeka State Journal* in 1955:[10]

ADMITTED AT 13, SHE LEAVES
STATE HOSPITAL AFTER 72 YEARS

Seventy-two years ago, a pale child of 13, daughter of a prominent Kansas family, was registered on the books at Topeka State Hospital. Friday, a little "dried up" old lady of 85, with no family around to remember, walked out to life on the outside.

It was a June day in 1882, the year a man by the name of Franklin D. Roosevelt was born, the year first diggings were being made on what was to be the Panama Canal, the year Arthur was President, that her name was written on the dusty books used then, three years after the hospital opened, to record patients.

"Pale, fair health, is cross, talks foolishly," said the admission record of number 313, the 313th patient to enter the hospital. Cause of insanity: "Sincerity and love of truth and finding that nearly everything was a lie."

Friday, with only a pair of blue eyes resembling the child who went in, a withdrawn, almost mute woman who can no longer talk of her years in the hospital, did something she had been wanting to do for years. She left the hospital for a nursing home.

We can try to console ourselves with the thought that most of this is a thing of the past, but that is simply not so. As President Kennedy pointed out, there are still state mental hospitals which remain largely custodial centers; they provide little treatment for a variety of reasons: inadequate professional staff, limited budgets, isolation of the hospitals from other medical centers, an apathetic public, and an overall defeatist attitude that the mentally ill are hopeless cases. Nor was Mr. Kennedy attempting exaggerated rhetoric for effect. His statement could be documented a thousand times over. Just recently a well-trained psychiatric aide reported one of her own experiences in a state school for the mentally retarded. She described her single-handed efforts which finally brought about the discontinuation of the practice of issuing each new patient, along with the clothes for daily use, a packet of clothes marked "death bundle." Enclosed in each packet were the clothes the person would be buried in—a stark reminder to each patient that there was only one way out of that particular institution. Let us also remember that there are untold numbers of human beings living out their lives in forgotten back wards of some of our monstrously large mental institutions. This neglect of our fellow man is our common shame, a shame that is incompatible with any illusory pursuit of "peace of mind."

Nor can we close our minds to the fact that not all mentally ill are in hospitals. Also, many circumstances of our culture aggravate the mental-health problem. We can almost foresee certain categories of people who will become mentally ill. Recently a national magazine, describing the frightening problem of high-school "dropouts," featured in an article a photograph of a group of young men who had quit school. Their faces mirrored the apathy of their existence, the loss of direction in their lives. The article described the potential loss to society in these young men, and the price they may come to pay in human suffering for their revolt of the moment. Such a problem is an aspect of the total mental-health problem. And the human family cannot afford many such losses. Pierre Teilhard de Chardin, reflecting on the barren life of the Chinese in the 1920s, was vividly aware of what this would cost all humanity—"To reach full maturity the earth needs every drop of its blood." [11]

We must not forget those born with various degrees of mental retardation, with or without accompanying physical handicaps. Increased research in this area gives us hope that better ways will be found to help them live successfully within the limits of their handicaps. One has only to read Pearl S. Buck's tender document about "the child who never grew," [12] to know the heartache of parents with a retarded child and the greater heartache at finding no adequate help to meet the child's special needs.

Medical science has added to man's longevity—and this, too, brings mental-health problems in its wake. "Senior citizenship" for some becomes a satisfying and happy period. For countless others it becomes a period of torture and misery, not because of physical decline but because of psychic suffering. To feel useless and unwanted, as so often happens with the elderly, is an acute form of suffering not treatable with a pill. We must help them to live rich, rewarding lives.

The role of illness in crime is a subject requiring attention. Locking up law offenders in prisons and "reformatories" has accomplished little, either for the offenders or for society. Many judges and lawyers have long recognized how illogical and ineffective this is. Some gains are being made, ever so slowly, in the re-examination of our whole penal system. The increasing cooperation between the law and psychiatry should result in the needed social reform of our whole approach to crime. And we can be honestly committed to such reforms without equating all crime with illness and without simply substituting hospitals for prisons.

We could fill the rest of this book by such a listing of potential areas of mental illness. Let us conclude our incomplete list by mentioning one more—leisure time. Since what is work and what is play is determined by one's attitude toward the activity, there are some people for whom work and play alike are richly satisfying. But in this nation, where there is increasing leisure time for many people, the psychiatrist knows that for many it comes not as a joy but as a burden. The problem of how to use leisure time for satisfying and constructive living is another part of our national mental-health program.

In the final analysis the national mental-health problem is not a single one, but a series of many problems—biological, psychological, sociological, educational, religious—all interrelated. Obviously the health professions, or the clergy, or the legislators, or even a militant citizens' group, cannot solve these problems alone. They must involve all of us. Clearly we do not expect priests and nuns to become mental-health "checkers" and "spotters" or to take up volunteer work in the local mental-health clinics. What we do expect is the cultivation of *attitudes* that will make them more alert to the problem—attitudes that they will take actively into their vocational work. Such attitudes must be founded on correct knowledge and information. In the next few chapters we shall attempt to elaborate some aspects of the complex problem of mental illness and consider some of the medical and allied professions' concerted efforts to alleviate it.

3

The Meaning of Mental Illness

In the opening section of *"Pacem in Terris,"* Pope John XXIII speaks of the providential order of the universe and of the even more wondrous order in man who, created in God's image and endowed with intelligence and freedom, is given the task of being lord of creation. But he notes, too, how strongly does "the turmoil of individual men and peoples contrast with the perfect order of the universe." [1] In man's nature are the potentialities for order, but also the capacities for this turmoil and destruction. Man is not a machine who can be governed by impersonal laws or irrational forces; neither is he an angelic being who can live independently of the material limits of space and time.

The Christian view of man stresses both the complexity and the unity of man's composite nature; essentially man is both body and soul, matter and spirit. His capacities and powers of knowing and loving must be developed, must grow and mature, as man freely opens himself more and more to reality. Man must become what he is. It is by human effort in cooperation with God's grace that man's uniquely human potentials must be realized in his growth toward maturity and wholeness.

Each person is unique among men, yet each human being shares in the essential nature of man. And there is a unity of human experience that should tell us of the basic intelligibility and continuity in the experiences of the human family. Yet we suspect that, if our readers reflect on their attitudes toward mental illness, they will see that this unity is often lost sight of. The tendency is strong in all of us to set off the mentally ill as entirely different from the rest of us. We find it difficult to acknowledge within ourselves the same potentialities for destruction and disorganization that characterize the behavior or fantasies of the mentally ill. This difficulty in turn leads to a common misconception of mental illness, a misconception that is often unchristian. Further, a certain basic humility is needed before one can disabuse himself of this false idea.

There is a growing movement today toward clarifying and conceptualizing the nature of mental illness which we feel comes closer to reality and is more consonant with the Christian view of man. Its thesis is this: mental health and illness are to be viewed in a unitary, holistic way; they are relative to each other, so that in a true sense we can all be said to be more or less mentally healthy or ill at a given moment. This does not blur the distinction between health and illness, but it sets them against the dynamics of one's experiences. One of the chief proponents of this thesis is Dr. Karl Menninger, who has devoted much of his life to elaborating and clarifying this unitary view in order to provide a more rational basis for the diagnosis and treatment of mental illness.[2] This view cuts through the therapeutic nihilism that so long dominated those whose approach to the mentally ill was restricted to classification and custody.

It is no easy task, however, to change the common misconceptions.[3] The belief persists that mental illness happens only to the "other guy," that the average person really has nothing in common with the "mentally ill." Many heroic efforts toward correcting these misconceptions have failed, despite the public-education programs of the National Association of Mental Health during the past fifty years.

Why is it so difficult to educate the public about this subject? It is not so hard to teach an intelligent audience that extreme human behavior—suicide, for example, or murder —is the product of mental illness; but to take the next step and disclose that everyone has something in common with the suicide or the murderer—this is far more difficult. Most people cannot face the fact that in every man there are raw, aggressive drives that have to be harnessed and so expressed that they at once are socially acceptable and conform to the deep, inner demands of human nature. Suicide or murder marks the failure of an individual to harness his destructiveness.

A favorite theme of the mental-health lecturer is that mental illness is only an exaggeration of ordinary or normal behavior, and that the behavior of the mentally ill differs from that of the healthy *in degree,* not in kind. He might draw a useful analogy from physics: the difference in electricity in lightning and in a light bulb is not in kind, but in the degree involved in each one. Some in his audience may gain from this a new and broader concept of mental illness. But all too often such an approach elicits only a "notional assent" of the hearers—to borrow Cardinal Newman's term. The acceptance is largely in the order of abstraction, with little or no application to one's own life situation. The "real assent" that involves the total person is lacking.

Does a shift of attitudes require a personal experience of

mental illness? We think not; but it frequently happens that way. Psychiatrists may not often say it out loud, but they are secretly pleased when priests, teachers, physicians, nurses, and others in the service professions come for help. With such a patient one of the by-products of treatment is often an increased compassion for emotional conflict and mental suffering, a greater capacity to understand and break through some of the myths about mental illness.

One of the many such myths, the most persistent, is that the mentally ill are very different from the rest of us. This myth is as stubborn as crab grass. Trying to stamp it out with education may bring a more rational understanding of mental illness; but often it elicits only a "notional assent." *This does not necessarily change one's attitude toward mental illness.* This is partially what frustrates every program of public education.

Is there a psychological explanation for this lack of reason in our attitudes? There is at least a partial one—our hidden fears. Have you ever asked yourself what it is that you fear most? Some will say death—although this may not be a very Christian answer. Others may specify some circumstances of death, such as its suddenness or violence in an airplane crash, for example, or in an automobile accident. Still others might express a lingering fear of some incurable disease, or of becoming a helpless invalid. A common denominator of all these fears is that they come from events we cannot prevent. Such fears arise when we reflect on how our world is indeed a dangerous place in which to live, that not even our homes are safe refuges from many external dangers.

While a psychiatrist admits to all such dangers and fears, he may not agree that this kind of danger provokes the most fear in people. A more basic fear is one that, curiously, people do not talk about very much, or, even more curiously, have perhaps never admitted. For example, a realistic fear of traffic dangers on the highway includes the fear that something might go wrong with the car, making it impossible to control the situation and to drive safely. There is a similar but deeper fear that we might lose control of ourselves and "go crazy." This fear seems to be the basis of the average individual's conception of a mentally ill person as one who has "gone crazy," who is "out of his head," who does not really know what he is doing, who is dangerous to be around and has to be locked up and restrained.

The prejudice in such an attitude was exemplified by the reaction of visitors shown through a large mental hospital where patients looked not unlike the visitors and were doing ordinary tasks, walking around freely, talking and laughing. Their behavior did not quite fit the popular notions of the mentally ill. Even seeing that the patients are not much different from themselves does not convince some. Invariably at the end of such a tour someone will ask, "But where do you keep the ones who are really sick—you know, the bad ones?" This implies, of course: "I came to see some crazy people. I am disturbed that they are not sufficiently different from me." One despairs at such resistance to public mental-health education. This is not to deny that some patients fit the popular image, are indeed "out of their minds" and "act crazy." But their number is small, and with modern treatments such acute suffering can usually be controlled as quickly as one can alleviate a high fever.

People persist in their misconception about mental illness sometimes out of their own psychological need for reassurance that they could never be mentally ill because they are so much more in control of themselves than the unfortunate "crazy" patients. A more far-fetched reason is that one born on the right side of the tracks or in a church-going family could not possibly become mentally ill. This, too, is a vain reassurance; mental illness occurs on both sides of the tracks and in members of all churches.

The durability of this wish to see the mentally ill as so different from the rest of us can, it seems, be best explained by the fear of the loss of control. This fear limits to the purely notional level one's acceptance of public-health educational efforts. Because of this fear also some city people are relieved, for example, if the state legislators plan to build a new mental hospital in the country rather than in town.

This difference between notional and real assent may be illustrated by a certain priest known for his militant efforts to refer people for psychiatric help. He was especially concerned that his parishioners should not be ashamed of their need for such help. Often he made the point that "mental illness is no different from physical illness in this regard. You go to a doctor if you have a bodily ailment; why shouldn't you seek medical treatment for psychic discomfort?"

The priest's assent, however, was merely notional. Later, he himself had to consult a psychiatrist for help with some personal difficulties. When an associate mentioned this fact to others, the priest exploded. Evidently he was unable to apply to himself what he applied to others. He even tried to attribute his emotional symptoms to some "gland trouble." However, in the course of his personal experience with the illness and treatment, he changed this attitude from the purely notional realm to a real assent.

The priest openly recognized the value of treatment—for others; he was ashamed to have his own need known. "Of course," it was said, "he probably wanted it concealed because of what his people might think if their parish priest was seeing a psychiatrist." This may be a correct interpretation of the circumstances, but that does not make the priest's attitude right. The priest's reaction was identical with that which he tried to correct in his parishioners. It is time for all of us not only to admit but to believe that there are all degrees of mental illness, that much of it is minor, and that most of it can be cured if adequate treatment is provided early. To achieve such a change in public attitude requires the efforts of responsible leaders, among both religious and laity, and cannot be achieved alone by those professionally engaged in mental-health work.

We plead, then, for a concept of mental illness that does not condemn many of our fellow men as totally different, so that they become "out of sight, out of mind" in mental hospitals. A concept of mental illness and mental health that embraces all of us is imperative. But before we present this concept more fully, let us consider a few historical vagaries of the tendency to categorize the ill and the well. This tendency seems as old as man himself, and it frequently took rather terrifying forms.

Man's unique capacity for comparing himself with others enables him to notice his likenesses to and differences from them. Undoubtedly this is one of the strong forces operating in the development of the child, as he takes on the manners and mores of parents, peers, teachers, and others. But more to the point here is man's inclination to set himself off from those who are different. And he may be more or less successful in explaining the differences.

Take, for example, a primitive man injured by a wild animal. Having suffered serious injuries—broken bones and torn flesh—he screamed with pain. Even primitive man could follow the series of cause and effect: injury, pain, reaction to pain. But an occasional primitive man suffering from a severe mental illness may have screamed as violently as the one torn by the wild beast. Here no cause was visible. The deranged person showed no injuries, no bleeding, no gaping wounds. His behavior confounded his fellow tribesmen. Some suspected a malevolent spirit was inside this man, torturing him so that he screamed wildly. Or, perhaps it was the revenge of a god who might be appeased by making a social outcast of the strangely acting madman. Apparently some "medical" efforts were made to cure the patient of the evil spirits molesting him by allowing their escape through holes bored in the victim's skull. This is a speculation of the medical historians made from the findings of skulls in which there were not only trephine holes but also evidence of bone regrowth around the opening, which would indicate that the "patient" survived the treatment.[4]

The leap from primitive to modern man spans many centuries, but views of mental illness changed very little. Modern man, it is true, ruled out evil spirits as the cause of mental illness and began to seek the cause in the human brain. His treatments, however, were hardly more civilized than those of primitive man. One example tells us of the routine practice of shaving the heads of patients and applying various irritants to help "cure" the brain disorder:

This was standard medical practice and regarded as an advance on the ancient method of simply removing the hair to give "the grosse vapours" offending the brain a chance to "fume out" (Lemnius, 1576). It was believed that the running sores caused by vesicants and other counter-irritants and by the making of setons and issues facilitated the discharge of noxious humors. The more purulent they became and the longer they discharged, the greater the expected therapeutic effect. As Fallowes put it [1705], his "Oleum Cephalicum . . . by raising some Pustules upon the Head . . . opens the Parts which are condens'd by the black Vapours . . . confirms the Texture of the Brain, strengthens the Vessels, and gives a Freedom to the Blood and Spirits inclos'd in them." [5]

Refinements followed, such as slitting the scalp and inserting peas in the wound, "which soon set up the needed suppuration as counter-irritation to the morbid process going on within the skull." [6]

The history of man is punctuated with many such incredibly misguided efforts to treat the mentally ill. Whether the mentally ill were seen as possessed by evil spirits, or as afflicted with punishment for their sins, or as suffering from an imbalance of body humors, these attempts at causal explanations were wrong. This is not to say that advanced psychiatric thinking has the final definitive explanation. But it is a step closer to the truth to admit that there is no such thing as "true madness," even in the most bizarre behavior, and that a causal explanation can be found within the psychological nature of man himself.

However, there is a dimension to the problem which concerns the Catholic reader—a theological dimension that transcends the psychiatric explanations of mental illness. For in Biblical theology we find a definite connection between sin, sickness, and Satan. Man is clearly set forth in Divine Revelation as "fallen man," as engulfed in primordial, spiritual chaos, cut off from God's friendship and, by that very fact, in disharmony with his own nature and his surroundings. As St. Paul reminds us, death—and sickness, both spiritual and physical, that leads to death—came into the world because of sin. Since Satan the Tempter—who in Catholic teaching is acknowledged as a spiritual reality—is connected with man's original fall, he is also connected in some way with sickness and death.

Hence, we find strongly etched in the Gospels, especially that of St. Mark, the connection between Christ's healing miracles and His power over the Prince of Darkness. Looking at reality through the eyes of faith, we cannot but conclude that there is indeed a connection between sin and sickness. Yet this connection is *not an equation.* Although a person afflicted with mental illness is seen as a descendant of Adam, a member of a fallen race, his illness is not to be viewed as a visible mark of personal guilt. Recall the Gospel incident when Christ was asked by his followers about a blind man they saw, "Who has sinned, this man or his parents?" Christ's answer was pointed: "Neither this man has sinned nor his parents. No. God simply wants to make use of him to reveal his ways" (John 9:1-3). What is revealed of God's ways touches on the theological mystery of evil and of God's mercy. When confronted with the theological dimension of evil, however, people have often been strongly tempted to equate illness—especially mental illness —with moral guilt or diabolic possession. This in turn may be a further reason for the tendency to set off the mentally ill from "the rest of us," almost in a pharisaic spirit: "Thank God I am not like those neurotics. If only they lived their religious life and had more faith, they would be freed of Satan's influence or of the moral disorder that causes their mental suffering and disturbed behavior!"

This, of course, is a distortion, theologically as well as

psychologically. That which frees man from moral evil is not mental health but God's grace. But the life of grace is not lived independently of man's psychological nature or of his relations to other persons. Hence, mental illness can be an obstacle and hindrance to one's living out his Christian vocation in response to God's grace. Grace builds on nature and perfects it, and the neglect of either takes its toll.

As long as the common misconceptions of mental illness prevail, we will be unrealistic in our approach to the mentally ill. As Father George Hagmaier expresses it:

> The philosopher continues to exhort such sufferers to "think positively, and use will power to snap themselves out of it." Some religionists say, "Forget psychiatry, and pray more." The courts profess to cure such mental disorders as juvenile delinquency, alcoholism, and sexual depravity by punishing and imprisoning. A wing of the medical profession, subtly denying the sensitive and spiritual character of human personality, hopes one day to cure *all* emotional derangements with drugs, brain surgery, electro-shock and other purely mechanical devices.[7]

Why do we insist that mental illness differs from "normal" conduct only in degree, and that it is incorrect to restrict it to extreme forms of behavior which are then explained away as products of evil and sin? Is it because all of us are more or less mentally ill, that none of us is healthy? Not at all. But illness and health *are* relative terms, and it is inadequate to define the one simply as the absence of the other. This is especially pernicious if illness is viewed as some static entity—pneumonia, a fractured leg, schizophrenia. On this assumption, if the pneumonia is cured, the bone-break healed, or the schizophrenic symptoms removed, the patient is healthy.

In nearly every large general hospital in this country at a

given moment nurses are administering first-class physical care to patients with broken legs. Yet many of these nurses have a concept of illness and health that limits their view to the broken bone. If the bone is realigned and given protection, and is healing, with pain easily controlled by mild analgesics, will the nurse notice that the patient may be far more sick with something other than his broken leg? He may be seriously depressed because his injury has kept him from work and he is unable to provide for his family. Is his depression a sickness? His medical chart will probably not reflect his emotional reaction to his original illness. Moreover, that emotion may not ever be recognized by those in charge of his care. Their concern is to heal a broken leg; in the meantime, the patient may suffer more acutely from something other than the broken leg, and regrettably it may elude those who take care of him.

Concern for the sick requires a broadened concept of what is illness and also a broadened concept of what is health. Many people whom the psychiatrist sees and treats are far healthier than those who seek no treatment. It is, first of all, a promising sign of health for a person to recognize that things are not going right and to seek help for his troubles. To hide troubles, to be too proud to admit that one cannot master alone some aspect of his living, is as senseless as not seeing the physician when one has a persistent bellyache.

In a dynamic sense, we are all more or less mentally ill or mentally healthy at a given moment. Every unwarranted outburst of anger, every moment of despair, every crushing breath of depression is a degree of illness, and every reader of this book has had some such "illness" within the past forty-eight hours! Admittedly, this last statement needs qualification. These discrete states could be called "illness" without implying that the person himself is ill to the point where treatment should be recommended. But when such actions or feelings or states persist, or become repetitive or compulsive or dominating, then more properly we are dealing with mental illness. We wish to think of mental illness not in terms of medical disease entities, but rather as some aspect of personality disorganization. In this perspective health and illness are seen as way stations on a continuum. One's behavior may fluctuate along this continuum, and hence be considered relatively healthy or ill. But a man's patterns of behavior are of great importance, and a given episode of behavior must be measured against such patterns to determine accurately the presence or absence of mental illness.

This point can bear repetition. We are not saying that every emotional outburst or momentary depression is to be classified as mental illness that calls for psychiatric treatment. Such an outburst, however, can be called illness, just as the common cold is. Further, like the common cold, it is an illness which a person can learn to handle by himself. Each sniffle or cough does not send a person off to a physician for help. Similarly, in our wider sense of the term "mental illness" there are manifestations which a person learns to handle with his own resources. And, to continue the analogy with physical illness, if the common cold develops into pneumonia, professional medical help is needed. Similarly, when emotional outbursts or depressions become persistent, chronic, crippling, or diminishing of one's personal development and functioning, they are indications of mental illness which will respond only to professional psychiatric help.

Underlying this view admittedly is a conflict theory of

human personality. Freudian in origin, it is not at all incompatible with the Christian view of man in all his complexity. Living, then, is viewed as the difficult art of coping with various conflicts, whether coming from within a person or from without. The health-illness continuum, however, allows a distinction between healthy management of the conflicts or a sick, disorganized, and costly mismanagement. The continuum is like a spectrum with clear reds or blues but also many less distinguishable shades of color. At one end of the spectrum is mental health; at the other is total personality disorganization which may lead to self-destruction. In between are all shades and degrees of organization or disorganization; as one moves away from the "health end" of the continuum, he repudiates reality more and more and takes a toll of his own self and of society.

The foregoing description is a simplified view of what Dr. Karl Menninger calls "a unitary concept of mental illness." He protests the fruitless labeling of mental illnesses as if they were disease entities:

> There are greater and lesser degrees of disorganization which are not difficult to recognize, and there are ways in which to describe them which do not have the pejorative and damning consequences of the prevalent jargon. Our disease names are associated in the popular mind with the awful, haunting specter of alienation and possession by devils, and once possessed, all hope is abandoned. I like to have my students think of the patient not as one afflicted with a certain disease for which he has to find a name and then begin to fight, but rather as a somewhat disorganized human being who has gotten crosswise with his fellows and with himself until he is increasingly uncomfortable and unacceptable. Not fighting but guiding is in order. Of course one can describe a "manic" or a

"depressed" or a "schizophrenic" constellation of symptoms, but what is most important about this constellation in each case? Not, we think, its curious external form, but rather what it indicates in regard to the process of disorganization and reorganization of a personality which is in a fluctuant state of attempted adjustment to environmental reality. Is the imbalance increasing or decreasing? To what is the stress related? What psychological factors are accessible to external modifications? What latent capacities for satisfaction in work, play, love, creativity are discoverable for therapeutic exploitation? Is a restoration or reconstruction of adjustment patterns developing? Can this be fostered by discriminating medical intervention? [8]

What the physician attempts in treatment and how he tries to understand the individual patient's problem are reserved for later chapters. But if mental illness is seen as *personality disorganization*, the psychiatrist must have some guidepost to what constitutes mental health, seen as *personality organization*. For the mental health of the patient is the goal of the physician's therapy. It is beyond the scope of this book to try to settle a very complex problem which has engaged the research efforts of many. Marie Jahoda in *Current Concepts of Positive Mental Health* attempts a comprehensive treatment of this problem.[9] If it is permitted for the moment to look aside from philosophical and theological implications, let us say that the psychiatrist takes something like the following view of mental health.

He recognizes that man has available two types of psychic energy—constructive and destructive. Psychic energy can be directed toward constructive and destructive ends. Man can harness his destructive energies and redirect them into constructive activities. Success in this is a constituent of mental health; failure spells mental illness. How is one to judge the degree of success or failure? One way is to study how a man expends his psychic energy. It is relatively easy to categorize his behavior under three major headings: loving, working, and playing. The objects of an individual's love include everything from God to his family, his friends, his associates, and so on. A person who can love, work, and play—who can do all these things in a satisfying way—will probably never need to see a psychiatrist.

This ability, then, to love, work, and play in a reasonably satisfying way can serve to measure mental health. But it is helpful also to consider a fourth category of human behavior that is usually symptomatic of illness—hating. Some people are unable to love, work, and play because they spend much of their energy in hating. Hate can be turned outward, to the destruction of something or someone outside the person, or it may be turned inward, that is, upon the self. The murderer, for example, is someone who is sick from hating. And the most common kind of murderer, as psychiatrists know, is not the person who kills another but the one who destroys himself, not so often by suicide as by behavior that is ultimately self-defeating. Such behavior abounds in alcoholism, reckless driving, neglect of physical health, and even resistance to education and direction. Although we are all self-destructive at times, most of us have positive investments in life that are more dominant than the forces of self-destruction.

Whatever the metaphysical nature of this destructive drive in man may be, its recognition is of great importance in the clinical work of psychiatrists. We believe that Father Alfred Delp, a victim of mass hatred, was vividly aware of man's destructive drive when he wrote these reflections:

The essential requirement is that man must wake up to the truth about himself. He must rouse his consciousness of his own worth and dignity, of the divine and human potentialities within himself, and at the same time he must master the undisciplined passions and forces which, in his name and by bemusing him with delight in his own ego, have made him what he is. This is not a disparagement of passions. Woe to the man who tries to live without any— that is the way to disintegration. Man must take himself as he is with all the undercurrents and the fire of his nature. But the destructive element in passions, the element which knows neither limit nor restraint, must be brought under control or it will tear man to pieces and destroy him. Man's passionate preoccupation with self must be subordinated; he must retain all the strength and fire of devoted human love but without the blindness, the irresponsibility, the lack of instinct that makes it destructive.[10]

We should further note that the concept of mental health and illness cannot be totally divorced from the question of values. When the psychiatrist speaks of health as a goal of therapy, he not only considers health as good, but in his own mind he has an image of what a healthy person's activities of love, work, and play should be. *However, a competent psychiatrist will also respect the values of his patient.* The fact that systems of value differ need not prevent reaching some agreement on what is health and illness. Marie Jahoda wisely points out, "Mental health is one good among many; it is not the incarnation of the ultimate good," and, further, "The search for values underlying mental health need not involve one in the megalomaniacal task of blue-printing the values for the distant future, or for all civilizations." [11]

Catholics know from revelation the ultimate meaning and destiny of man; we have before us the risen Christ, both as a model and as an active, present cause of our fulfillment of that destiny. Our faith tells us boldly: "unless you are a man as Christ was a man, you are a failure." Christ's attitudes and values, made possible through the Christ-life of Grace, enable us to "put on Christ" more and more in a deepening faith, a stronger hope, and a more living love. But this supernatural life of grace builds upon the natural. Without in any way equating sanctity and mental health or making moral evil the equivalent of illness, we can still legitimately seek the limited goal of mental health as we have described it. And we can share this quest with others who may not have the same values or the same faith. Again, to cite Marie Jahoda, "There are . . . other good things in life, apart from mental health." And when we speak of someone as mentally ill, that means "neither condemning him to a mental hospital nor establishing his moral inferiority." [12]

Finally, we hope that as we broaden our concept of mental illness and mental health and begin to understand the goals of psychiatric treatment, we will see that there are clear grounds for a common concern, shared by both the religious and the mental-health professions. This is summed up succinctly in the words of Father John Ford, S.J.:

Mental hygiene and Christian asceticism both must deal with human passions and emotions, especially the disorderly ones. The spiritual father looks at these latter as the result of original sin, as the sources of sin and imperfections. The psychiatrist and psychologist look at them from the viewpoint of mental and emotional health. But fortunately, there need not be and in fact is not, in my opinion, any substantial conflict between the goals of Christian asceticism and those of mental hygiene. Indeed it is remarkable how modern ideals of mental health coincide with ancient ideas of holiness.[13]

4

Dimensions of Psychiatric Theory

Given a broadened concept of mental illness, we can be quite certain that the prevalence of such illness is as ancient as the history of man. It has always been necessary for man to cope with the demands of his internal environment—his inner needs—and with his external environment—the world around him. Since failures in such coping can lead to mental illness, we can assume that mental illness is hardly a phenomenon only of modern times. Despite the reach of such illness into antiquity, psychiatry as a medical specialty is of relatively recent origin. This is not to deny that frequent attempts were made in the past to understand and give medical treatment to mental illness. Some of these attempts showed flashes of insight; others were all too often marked by tragic misunderstanding and ignorance.

Psychiatry has been called the "Cinderella of medicine." [1] So long the neglected stepchild in the family of medicine, suddenly, in the twentieth century, psychiatry was transformed into a princess, commanding attention from the medical profession and the general public alike. Why this sudden transformation? One of the reasons is that, although there were periodic attempts to explain mental illness and rare attempts to cure it, there was the persistent, almost compelling tendency to think of illness in terms of the bodily organism alone. The very term *mental* illness did not fit any medical model. Mind-body relationships, of course, had interested philosophers and poets for centuries, but they were not an essential concern of physicians. Medicine lacked a scientific theory of human behavior that would begin to incorporate the subtle and complex body-mind relationships, both psychological and physiological, as they are manifested in exaggerated and "crazy" behavior as well as in so-called "normal" behavior. Once such a theory was developed, psychiatry began to contribute to a deeper understanding of illness and health.

Prior to this transformation of modern psychiatry, there was a defeatist attitude toward caring for the mentally ill. The prevailing assumption was that mental illness is irreversible. Curiously, this assumption long remained unchallenged and unexamined—by the very men who must have observed changes in themselves and in their environment. But no such change could be comprehended for the mentally ill. "Madness" was considered an incurable condition.

As long as this assumption prevailed, hardly any thought was given to treatment. Institutions were established to isolate the mentally ill from the rest of society. When a person's sickness became intolerable to his environment, he was simply shut up in a human warehouse where, more often than not, he was neglected, mistreated, and mocked by his fellow men who were on the "outside." Sunday visiting to see the inmates at the asylum was a sport for the curious and not unlike visiting the zoo. The cruelty to the mentally ill locked in "hospitals," behind bars, often in chains, is one of the more tragic chapters in the human record. To consider such places as treatment centers would be as misleading as to consider our present-day prisons as correctional institutions.

The few physicians who concerned themselves with the mentally ill developed inadequate or erroneous theories about mental illness which further shackled these patients. It was in the name of medical science that they were considered untreatable. It was believed that they were the victims of an organic brain disease which made them behave differently. When the microscope and modern methods of studying the cells of the body tissues came along, the brains of the deceased mentally ill were examined with the hope that the area of pathology which had caused the derangement would be found. But the search was in vain; no demonstrable structural differences could be found between the brains of the mentally ill and those of the healthy.

As long as mental illness was thought to be caused by brain diseases, it was considered incurable. Soon the emphasis on heredity was used to buttress the attitude that treatment was of no use. When it was known that a patient's father was alcoholic, it was thought that this fact explained the patient's illness. Somehow it was overlooked that many persons whose fathers drank excessively did not become mentally ill. The statement, "You know, there is mental illness in the family," is rather simple-minded, because it is doubtful that one could trace any family very far before finding someone so afflicted.

In 1857, Bénédict-Augustin Morel, a physician, named the most common serious mental illness *dementia praecox*. By this term he meant to indicate two things: that it was a disease of the young, usually beginning in the teens of the patient's life; and that it progressed to a demented state.

Since this latter was seen as the result of a progressive deterioration of the brain, there was obviously no treatment for it and the only "solution" was to lock up such people in institutions. Morel was wrong. But it took a long time for even the medical profession to become convinced of this, so much so that even today some remain pessimistic.

From the first institutions for the mentally ill to the modern psychiatric hospital lies a long trail of human misery and neglect. In the late eighteenth century a new kind of guide appeared and a new trend began—there were great humanitarians who spoke of kindness and charity for the mentally ill. Such was the nature of the Frenchman Philippe Pinel, who, as superintendent of the asylums Bicêtre and Salpêtrière, broke the chains that bound the helpless victims of mental illness. Then William Tuke and a small group of Quakers in England started a hospital for the mentally ill and called it "The Retreat"—perhaps one of the most beautiful names ever given a mental hospital. Patients were treated with kindness and love. Yet their illness was not understood. There was no theory of mental illness that made any sense. But the patients were seen as suffering human beings whose dignity should be respected. And something of a miracle happened: *some of the patients got well.*

We noted in Chapter 2 that Albert Deutsch studied the state mental hospitals in the United States in the 1940s and branded them as "the shame of the states." At one time they could well have been our pride. The United States had some good mental hospitals in the early nineteenth century. The treatment was called "moral treatment."

Humanitarianism favored the view that lunatics had undergone stresses which robbed them of their reason. That such stress could result from disappointment as well as inflammation was a basic assumption. Stresses of a psychological nature were referred to as *moral causes*. Treatment was called *moral treatment*, which meant that the patient was made comfortable, his interest aroused, his friendship invited, and discussion of his troubles encouraged. His time was managed and filled with purposeful activity. . . .

Moral treatment was never clearly defined, possibly because its meaning was self-evident during the era in which it was used. In the context of that era it meant compassionate and understanding treatment of innocent sufferers.[2]

This meant that patients were seen as sick people. Consequently, it was believed that they should be housed in a pleasant environment and provided with stimulating and interesting things to do, and particularly that they should work. And many of them got well.

But then came an Industrial Revolution, a rapidly growing population with ever-increasing immigration, and a Civil War. The idea got lost that "no hospital should be bigger than that in which the superintendent can know each patient personally" [3]—and monstrous institutions grew and grew with thousands and thousands of patients, sent there to die. The gains of the great humanitarian physicians were rapidly lost. The organic theory of etiology of mental illness came again into full sway. Young physicians avoided psychiatric work, unwilling to face patients who they had been taught were hopeless. The quality of care sank lower and lower.

By the 1940s, one of the most shameful aspects of American life was our state hospitals—all of them.[4] Kansas can be given as an example. In 1949, when incensed citizens decided to do something about their state hospitals, there were over two thousand patients in the Topeka State Hospital. There were two physicians, and neither had any special training in psychiatry, and there was *not a single registered nurse working in the hospital*. The patients were cared for by attendants, many of them loyal and devoted, who were trying to do a job without training, without supervision, and without anyone to give them support and encouragement; there were also other attendants who were brutal and exploitative. But Kansas, with a number of other states, was able to take steps toward remedying this situation. That they all could do so was the mark of a new spirit of hope for treating the mentally ill.

This spirit came from the dramatic discoveries about psychiatric treatment which were made long before 1949, not in a psychiatric hospital but in a physician's office in Vienna. The new hope was a result of the work of Sigmund Freud. Freud's office was his laboratory; his instruments were his own scientific curiosity and his insight into the complexities of human development and behavior; he studied the mentally ill patients who came to him for help; his technique of study and treatment came to be called psychoanalysis. Freud died, at the age of eighty-three, in 1939. By then more and more physicians were studying his writings and discovering that he had left a scientific heritage of great importance for understanding and treating the mentally ill. Freud himself had not seen large numbers of patients; he had never worked in a psychiatric hospital. But his theory of mental illness has contributed perhaps more toward alleviating human suffering than the work of any physician who ever lived.

What were some of Freud's basic theoretical formulations which enabled psychiatry to come of age? First, a theory of "causation" had to be elaborated that would take in *all* human behavior, even the most bizarre and insane. Prior to

Freud there were literary men who had recognized that a large area of the human personality lay outside conscious awareness, and that this part of the mind is often a propelling force in human conduct.[5] Freud did not discover the unconscious, but his scientific scrutiny of the unconscious aspects of human behavior marked the long-delayed beginning of the development of a scientific psychiatry. Not many people —not even many physicians—accepted this theory with any eagerness. To a world still smarting under the sting of Darwin's bold views, which seemed to challenge man in his uniqueness in the biological world, a further insult from a little-known Viennese neurologist was hardly welcome. Philosopher Alden L. Fisher speaks of Freud's

> significant but dangerous insight that the unconscious conflicts discovered as the source of his patients' illness were in principle shared by himself and all men. The insight is significant because it provides the ground, in principle, for psychoanalysis to become a general psychology of human behavior. It is dangerous because it deals a serious blow to the proud image of man as fully rational by right and not by effort.[6]

Yet, who would listen to a man who said his scientific data made it necessary to abandon the long-held notion that all man's motivations were apparent to his consciousness? Indeed, many people still find it hard to accept the theory of the unconscious, though for physicians and others it has introduced hope into the treatment of the mentally ill. Such physicians, now assuming that the patient's strange behavior does have a cause and an explanation, even if such may not be initially apparent either to patient or doctor, can hope to unlock the "secret" of this cause so that rational methods of treatment can be pursued.

Another of Freud's contributions to psychiatric understanding was his insight into the genesis of the human personality. Contrary to the popular belief that adolescence was the decisive formative period of personality, Freud pointed out that the major dispositions of personality development were established in infancy and early childhood. What may now seem commonplace and obvious was not so before Freud—namely, that the human personality unfolds around the basic realities of man's biology and the process of his socialization. This, of course, does not mean that the development of a man's personality can be reduced to these realities, but it does mean that to neglect their importance is to misunderstand man. For example, the fact that an infant is born helplessly dependent upon someone else turns out to be extremely important for understanding his later struggles with dependence and independence. This is not to say that Freud was the first to discover the importance of the mother-child relationship, for this had long been known. Again, it was a question of focus and detail and emphasis. It was not until Freud turned his clinical eye to this question that we could begin to understand that, since this was the child's first human relationship, its shadow would fall ever after on all his other human relationships.

A third contribution of Freud to the theory of personality and to psychiatry was his conception of the instinctual drives and their operation in human behavior. Freud modified his thinking along this line, as further observations and clinical data demanded. In the end he spoke of man's instinctual energies as being of the two kinds we have mentioned— the one directed toward constructive, and the other toward destructive, outlets. The constructive energies are manifested in the individual's capacity to love, the destructive in his tendency to hate. Psychiatrists began to view human suffering and mental illness in the light of these two drives and their interrelationships. When the psychiatrist speaks of love and hate in infants, these terms must not be given the moral overtones of adult life; yet the equilibrium of these forces in infancy and childhood has a bearing on the adult's capacity for love and hate. The disequilibrium seems to be a common denominator of mental illness. But it is not difficulty with loving too much that brings patients to psychiatrists; mental illness is characterized by an inability to control one's capacity for hating, whether it be directed at self or at others.

We might note here that this theory of the dual instinctual drives is used by many psychiatrists as a basis for treatment. The psychiatrist is concerned about how man lives with the destructive drive. The psychological health of the person appears to lie in his capacity to harness and channel his destructive energies, to make them subserve constructive ends. Perhaps a simple example from childhood, which many of us have experienced, will demonstrate the model upon which this harnessing of destructiveness can take place. To the great regret of harassed mothers, none of us is born with our present attitude toward dirt; this attitude was ever so slowly taught us, primarily by our mothers. Not a few of us were guilty of incidents in our childhood where we muddied up the side of a freshly painted house. A wise mother, recognizing the child's fun, may direct his energy (the same energy) to making mud pies or to using finger paints or crayons. Unacceptable behavior is made acceptable; the destructive energies are appropriately channeled.

Freud developed many other theoretical constructs about the human personality, including theories of symptom formation and of treatment. During the latter period of his career he turned his attention from man's instinctual life to the structure and dynamic functioning of the total human psyche. The complex psychic organization that evolves as the child matures must be adequate for the struggle with and direction of the instinctual drives, and must also adapt to the demands of reality and remain loyal to the individual's moral code. This later development in Freud's psychoanalytic theory is technically referred to as "ego psychology," in contrast to his earlier contribution, which is known as "instinct (or depth) psychology."

The further development of ego psychology by Anna Freud, Heinz Hartmann, Ernst Kris, Rudolph M. Loewenstein, David Rapaport, Erik H. Erikson, and others has opened up the possibilities for a more intelligible integration of psychoanalytic theory and a Christian philosophy of man. Once a mechanistic model of man is abandoned—it was such a model that in the past lent itself to a "reductionistic" view, wherein every aspect of human personality is reduced to some common denominator of the animal world—then the valid insights of contemporary psychoanalytic theory can be incorporated into a richer and more profound understanding of man. For example, Alden L. Fisher notes of the formulations of Hartmann, a contemporary "ego psychologist," that they "show promise of even greater theoretical recognition and exploitation of the concrete workings of genuine human freedom." [7]

Many of the ideas thus far treated in this chapter are sometimes lumped under the one word "psychoanalysis." This term has its origin in Freud's work. In popular usage, however, its meaning is frequently confused. It may help dispel some of the confusion to realize that psychoanalysis is several things. First, the term can refer to a body of theoretical ideas laboriously derived from clinical experience. Freud contributed the major fabric of this "psychoanalytic theory" of human personality, but by no means did he say the last word; many others have embellished the theory, deepened the perspective, and balanced the pattern with their own original contributions and insights. An example is the developments in ego psychology referred to above. It is safe to say that this cumulative working theory of personality is the frame of reference most widely used by present-day American psychiatrists and the other behavioral scientists.

Psychoanalysis is, second, the term applied to a special method of treatment developed by Freud. He early discovered that there were roads to the human unconscious, wherein lay many of the secret but truculent conflicts that caused painful symptoms. From simply listening to his patients Freud learned the importance of "free association." If a patient is allowed to talk freely, he begins to associate various ideas—from dreams, memories, and the like—and gradually recalls items from the forgotten past which, though at first seemingly unrelated to the original train of thought, turn out to be related in the unconscious. Thus Freud found a way to the unconscious, where memories and conflicts were buried but not dead and hence could be productive of symptoms. He found further that he achieved best results with this method if he saw the patient frequently —as many as five one-hour periods a week. This process of treatment, however, was quite extended; it took many such analytic hours to work through the patient's problems.

In connection with psychoanalysis as a method of treatment, one of Freud's great contributions was his discovery of the nature and importance of "transference." This is a technical concept which cannot be adequately dealt with in this book. Suffice it to say that Freud learned that the patient, attempting to grapple with his emotional problems, gradually begins to experience, in the encounter with the analyst, feelings that have little to do with the reality of the analysis itself. These feelings, which the patient once actually felt toward significant figures in his past, are relived during the treatment. It is precisely the analysis and understanding of these emotional reactions that become the core of the psychoanalytic treatment.[8]

Although psychoanalysis can be an excellent method of treatment in competent hands, it is unfortunately hemmed in by many limitations. There is, worst of all, the paucity of trained analysts, whose education is long and costly. In the United States today there are less than two thousand psychoanalysts. Also, not all mentally ill persons are able to cooperate in this treatment; clinically speaking, it is the most appropriate one for only a relatively small number of patients. In addition, psychoanalysis is expensive and time-consuming, and demands a long dedication on the part of the patient and therapist alike.

Besides referring to a personality theory and a method of treatment, the term "psychoanalysis" can also refer to a research tool. This cuts across the other two meanings, for within the method itself research can be carried on to enlarge the understanding of personality. Hence, although few patients are actually in psychoanalysis, the majority who are presently in psychiatric treatment are receiving therapy based on the insights about human behavior which are a part of the system of psychology known as psychoanalysis.

There is another term on the lips of many which can also generate a certain amount of confusion—the adjectival form of Freud's name. Every now and then a psychiatrist is asked, "Are you a Freudian?" The psychiatrist's usual embarrassment at the question tends to confirm the questioner's suspicion of something sinister. But the psychiatrist is embarrassed not for himself but for the questioner; he is concerned about how to answer this awkward question without making the other party appear foolish. To ask a psychiatrist if he is Freudian is, in a sense, tantamount to asking a doctor if he is an Oslerian, a Galenian, or a Virchowian.* In reality if a psychiatrist is at all competent and loyal to his science, he is not "anything-ian"—he is "everyone-ian"! When faced with a suffering patient he uses whatever scientific knowledge he has in order to help him, regardless of who contributed the specific bit of knowledge to his science. Most physicians carry a stethoscope for listening to the heart and lungs; it would be as appropriate to ask a physician if he is therefore a Laënnecian** as it is to ask if he is a Freudian because he keeps the writings of Freud on his bookshelves.

Being not much different from other people, physicians tend to honor the great men in the history of their profession. Freud's stature in psychiatry is unequaled, so it is not surprising to find psychiatrists interested in the writings and the person of Sigmund Freud. Some may not like him, but even they cannot ignore him. If they do admire and study

---

* William Osler (1849-1919) was one of the most influential physicians of his generation and a famous diagnostician and teacher. Galen (c.130-c.200) was an important figure in the history of medicine. For fourteen centuries physicians followed his teachings. Rudolf Virchow (1821-1902) did work on cellular pathology that made the entire medical world his disciples.

** René Laënnec (1781-1826) invented the stethoscope about 1819.

him, we should not be surprised at the display of a picture of Freud in the doctor's office. If that constitutes being a Freudian, well and good. But when we see other pictures— a John Hunter, an artist's conception of Hippocrates, a photo of Lincoln or Dostoevsky—perhaps the original awkward question may come more haltingly to the lips.

There is an even more awkward question that is frequently put to a Catholic psychiatrist: "How do you square Freud's teachings with Catholic doctrine?" The answer is quite simple: "We do not." A friend of ours once suggested a devastating counter-question: "How do you square St. Thomas's teachings with Catholic doctrine?" The collected works of many a Catholic writer may well contain errors. It is well known that St. Thomas, for example, did not accept Our Lady's Immaculate Conception. True, our analogy may limp. The over-all orthodoxy of the Angelic Doctor is recognized by all. But Freud was pioneering in a new area of investigation. Being a child of his times, he brought to his study many assumptions that would be unacceptable to Catholic thought. But that does not vitiate the basic discoveries about the way the mind works.

All too frequently among Catholic writers we find an uncritical rejection of psychiatric literature simply because it is not congenial to one's way of thought. For example, an editor in his introduction to a translation of a French series called "Psychoanalysis and Conscience" makes this statement:

> Those who pursue these studies should bear in mind that the average psychiatrist takes no account of the human soul and that, ignorant of its faculties, intellect and will, he is incapable of interpreting his observations in terms of them. This being the case, it is hardly surprising that so

many fall into error and that the end term of so much psychiatric practice is to devalue human liberty and to declare the sinlessness of the aberrations described.[9]

This type of generalization is to be regretted. If the statement were simply that the average psychiatrist does not think in Aristotelian-Thomistic terms, we would agree; for such a person might not be trained in this philosophical tradition. Nevertheless, any psychiatrist worthy of the name confronts the whole man; and if he neglects the deeper aspects of man as a cognitive and conative being he is a poor psychiatrist. Further, if he reduces man to the level of an instinct-driven, totally determined being he is a poor "philosopher"—or rather, he has not examined his own philosophical assumptions.[10] But if he confronts the whole man in all his mystery and misery, he cannot but be concerned with the deeper aspects of human nature. He might not speak in Scholastic terms, but when, for example, he attempts a diagnostic examination of the patient's perception, intellection, emotion, action, integrative processes, and the like, he is trying to deal with man in his totality.[11] And the psychiatrist is very much concerned with strengthening the patient's internal freedom and sense of responsibility, although he may not speak in terms of free will and the spiritual nature of man.

Rightly then does a recent writer score the irresponsibility of some of the current Catholic criticism of psychiatry which "unfortunately, but perhaps not too surprisingly, . . . is equated with *the* Catholic view."

> . . . when one Catholic philosopher . . . suggests that the empirically verified findings of psychoanalysis must be accepted or rejected to the degree that they can be shown to be dialectical extensions of Aristotle's treatise

on the soul, I think the psychoanalyst has good grounds
for irritation and vigorous opposition." [12]

We are in favor of listening to what psychiatric theory can
tell us about some of the deeper aspects of the human person.
When St. Thomas synthesized some of the profound insights of Aristotelian philosophy with Christian thought, he
met much opposition for tapping sources of thought that
were branded as pagan. Yet man's understanding of man did
not end with St. Thomas. And, whatever one may think of
modern psychiatric views, he cannot in justice ignore them
or dismiss them *a priori* as being somehow or other pagan
or unworthy of further consideration.

The philosophical and theological implications of psychiatric theory demand much further study. In this chapter we
have tried simply to point up a few aspects of psychiatry
and some attitudes about it. If for no other reason than that
psychiatry has brought hope and help to the mentally ill,
we should be interested in what it has to say.

In this spirit we endorse Jerome Bruner's summation of
Freud's contribution:

> . . . It is our heritage from Freud that the all-or-none
> distinction between mental illness and mental health has
> been replaced by a more humane conception of the con-
> tinuity of these states. The view that neurosis is a severe
> reaction to human trouble is as revolutionary in its impli-
> cations for social practice as it is daring in formulation.
> The "bad seed" theories, the nosologies of the nineteenth
> century, the demonologies and doctrines of divine punish-
> ment—none of these provided a basis for compassion to-
> ward human suffering comparable to that of our time.
> . . . Freud's sense of the continuity of human conditions,
> of the likeness of the human plight, has made possible a
> deeper sense of the brotherhood of man. [13]

A greater compassion toward human suffering and a deeper sense of the brotherhood of man are certainly of central importance to any who are sincerely attempting to live a Catholic life.

5

Psychiatric Practice—
Diagnosis and Treatment

The diagnosis and the treatment of mental illness are intimately intertwined. In the finest tradition of medicine, diagnosis always precedes treatment. However, in psychiatry both treatment and diagnosis begin when the patient starts his first appointment. During this first hour the patient has a chance to tell someone his problem, which in itself may relieve some of his suffering. But, however eager the physician is to relieve the patient of his distress, he has the prime duty of finding out what the problem is—that is, of diagnosing the illness.

It simply is not possible for a psychiatrist to understand the patient's problem in a few minutes. Although the treatment begins with the first hour, the prescription of a detailed plan for it must await an adequate diagnostic study. Quick diagnostic studies are always suspect. Hurried planning is more often than not doomed to fail. It is sometimes hard for patients and their relatives to accept the length of time required for a proper diagnostic study and also for psychiatric treatment. But the psychiatrist knows that he must stand up to their impatience. Failure to do so can only mean that his patient will be short-changed. People do not change quickly; it takes time, and hasty psychiatry flirts with being poor psychiatry.

After one or more interviews with the patient, the experienced psychiatrist may have a full enough understanding of the patient's problem to prescribe treatment accurately. Or he may require a psychological test study to enlarge his conception of the patient's illness. Further, since nearly every patient is a member of a family unit, his illness affects the other members and, in turn, their reactions to his illness affect him. Because of this, the psychiatrist may also talk with the patient's relatives as part of a diagnostic examination. Or he may ask for the help of a psychiatric social worker whose specialty is working with the families of the mentally ill. In major psychiatric clinics psychiatrists, clinical psychologists, and psychiatric social workers join together as a diagnostic team. The more complicated the illness, the more likely the psychiatrist will want the help of these colleagues to arrive at an accurate diagnosis.

Most readers would be curious to know what takes place when a diagnostic team gets together to discuss their examination of a patient. Short of actually attending such a conference—which alone can convey the experience adequately —some flavor of it may be caught vicariously in a descriptive account. Despite the limitations of such a narrative, the following is offered as a portrayal of an outpatient diagnostic team conference. After having examined the patient for several days, the team members have met to discuss their findings and to plan a treatment program. The conference is in progress:

DOCTOR JONES (psychiatrist): During the past week, Doctor Smith, you have been completing a psychological test study of our patient, Miss Jackson, and I have been seeing her in a series of clinical psychiatric interviews. Concurrently, Miss Williams has seen the patient's brother in a number of social-work interviews. Today we can pool our findings and begin to prescribe a treatment program for Miss Jackson. You may remember that we thought in our first conference that Miss Jackson would require hospitalization during the early part of her treatment. When she is admitted to the hospital, Doctor Moore will be the psychiatrist in charge of her treatment. I have asked him to join us today so that he will know the results of our examination. Doctor Smith, have you completed the psychological test study?

DOCTOR SMITH (clinical psychologist): I finished the study yesterday afternoon. In spite of her obvious distress and disorganization, Miss Jackson spared no effort in working on the tests, demanding a great deal of herself.

DOCTOR JONES: As a matter of fact, she demands too much of herself. But before we talk more about our findings, let us remind ourselves of what we know about Miss Jackson's life and the circumstances which brought her here. She is a thirty-nine-year-old unmarried schoolteacher who was referred to us by her family physician. Our internist has completed a physical examination and the necessary laboratory studies and reports that the patient is in excellent physical health. Our neurologist has completed a neurological examination and finds no evidence of physical disease of the nervous system. During the psychiatric interviews, Miss Jackson was very tense and agitated. She rambled on and on in telling me about herself, often becoming lost in minor details. From the little she has actually told me, it is almost impossible for me to reconstruct what has been going on in her life recently. It is apparent that the patient had been an able and competent schoolteacher, but, for reasons that were not easily learned from my initial interviews with her, she has become increasingly disorganized and confused. Miss Williams, you have talked with the patient's brother; what have you learned from him?

Miss Williams (psychiatric social worker): The brother says she has been very successful as a grade-school teacher. She has lived for many years by herself in a little house near the school. She manages very frugally, protecting a small inheritance from her father. The brother first became concerned about his sister a few months ago—at the time that their mother fell and fractured her pelvis, an injury requiring prolonged nursing care. Over the protest of her brothers and sisters, our patient insisted on taking her mother into her home, arranged for a practical nurse during the day when she was at work, and often spent much of the night in caring for her mother and in doing the housework. Not long after her mother moved into her home, Miss Jackson began to become moody and preoccupied. She avoided the few friends she had and was less active in her clubs. Once she completely forgot to arrange for a PTA program for which she had assumed responsibility, an action which seemed to everyone to be "most unlike her." The brother says the patient gradually became more and more disorganized and less able to meet her teaching responsibilities. The last month of the school year her classroom was undisciplined and the children complained about her irritability. After school was out, she spent most of her time in her bedroom. She would tell visitors that people were talking about her and were making critical remarks about the way she looked after her mother. She became afraid that something dreadful would happen to her mother and anxiously checked on her many times during the night. The mother became alarmed about her when Miss Jackson spoke of having a bad disease that was contaminating the entire neighborhood. When the mother told this to her son, he immediately notified the family physician, who referred the patient to us.

DOCTOR JONES: So the history is that of a progressive personality disorganization. Doctor Smith, what is the nature of the disorganization in mental functioning that you are seeing on the tests?

DOCTOR SMITH: Miss Jackson is clearly of superior intelligence, although each of the tests showed the severe stress that she is experiencing and its seriously disorganizing effect upon her. She was forgetful, easily distractible, she misheard instructions, and had much difficulty concentrating upon the tests. Despite her obvious confusion, we saw much evidence of the orderly, meticulous woman that she must have been before this illness, although now, at her worst moments, she often founders helplessly, immobilized by self-doubts and indecisiveness.

DOCTOR JONES: Could you give an example of these two features of her thinking—the meticulousness on the one hand, and the confusion and disorganization on the other?

DOCTOR SMITH: Yes. When I asked her how many weeks there are in a year, she replied, "Fifty-six, I think. No, that's not right. Oh, dear, isn't that awful? I just can't seem to keep my head clear to think about things these days. Days? There are three hundred and sixty-five days in a year. That's what you asked, isn't it?" The next day she began the testing session by saying, "When you asked me about the year and I told you three hundred and sixty-five, I should have said three hundred and sixty-five and one-fourth because every year there is an extra quarter of a day. That's why we have leap year every four years." Even when she solved problems correctly, she complained about the length of time it took her to get the answer. Her many comments about her inability to think made clear her feeling that in her own eyes she could produce nothing of worth or merit. On one task, where she was asked to copy a group of nine simple geometric drawings, she spent twenty minutes in painful erasures and redrawings (most patients easily complete the task in five minutes), as though she expected herself to make printing-press-quality reproductions.

DOCTOR JONES: Do you remember that session when you gave her the arithmetic problems on the Wechsler-Bellevue Test and she became confused and wanted to give up? You led her back to the problems and helped to keep her at the task. I saw her immediately after that and she felt relieved and reassured that you had not let her just give up, and she even managed a wry smile as she said, "Imagine, Doctor Smith had to keep me on the job. That's the first time in my life anybody has had to keep *me* at something." With this came a great deal of material about what a hard-working, overly conscientious woman she has always been and some hints at how deeply angry she is over her rather cheerless and ungratifying existence.

DOCTOR SMITH: The projective tests—Rorschach, Word Association, and Thematic Apperception tests—help to show us just how strong this mild-looking woman's unresolved resentment really is. On the Rorschach ink blots, which are subject to an almost infinite variety of interpretations, this soft-spoken, meek woman consistently saw images which were blatantly aggressive and destructive in connotation. On the Word Association Test she had trouble in responding to each of the aggressive words like "hit," "fist," and "attack," constantly avoiding or denying the idea that she might have any angry thoughts or feelings. There were such reactions as these: "Hit"—there was a long delay, the patient looked upset and finally said, "I never hit anybody in my life. I never wanted to hit anybody, that's all I can think of, I can't get a word." When I said "Fist," she said, "Wrist? Wristwatch. You said wrist, didn't you?" "Attack" —the patient blushed and after a long delay said, "Newspaper," and made a vague, incoherent reference to a newspaper story she had read many months ago involving a sexual assault. When I asked her about this story, she became confused and rather angry, saying, "Why do they print such things in the newspapers?" At this point she gave vent to an angry, confused tirade about the "evil-mindedness" of the editor, publisher, and staff of her city newspaper.

MISS WILLIAMS: You know, Miss Jackson's brother says that she has always read all of the stories of murder, assault, and so on, in the newspapers. She has consistently deplored these, and once tried to get a group together to demand the suppression of such news, but at the same time she has talked and read and thought more about these topics than most people do.

DOCTOR JONES: I'm very glad that her brother could be here for this examination. What clues do the tests give about why and at whom this woman is so deeply angry?

DOCTOR SMITH: Some evidence from the Word Association Test and the Thematic Apperception Test helps to clarify the guilt-arousing combination of love and resentment (of which she is mostly unaware) that characterizes Miss Jackson's relationship with her mother. To all of the words on the Word Association Test connoting parent-child relationships—words like "mother," "child," "daughter"—she responded, "Love," anxiously insisting that parents love their children, children in turn love their parents and take care of them, and that she especially loved, revered, and respected her aging mother. But on one picture in the Thematic Apperception Test she told a story of a girl who gave up marriage, job, and travel opportunities to stay home and care for a demanding, invalided mother.

Miss WILLIAMS: Just as her own life has been.

DOCTOR SMITH: Yes, but in the safety of a made-up story and speaking through the girl in the picture, Miss Jackson tells us of her hidden anger at her martyr-like existence and her unrecognized wish to have a life more independent of her mother.

DOCTOR JONES: It would seem, then, that Miss Jackson is a seriously disturbed woman who is having a great deal of difficulty maintaining her balance in the face of disorganizing anxiety about her angry impulses and feelings that are alien to her conscious mind. Her usual ways of dealing with a long-standing pattern of unresolved anger toward her mother—such as denying its existence, or continuous self-effacing sacrifice—seem now to have failed her, and she feels guilty without knowing why. And temporarily she has been driven to more desperate measures—including some clear-cut distortions of reality.

DOCTOR MOORE: The security of the hospital, with its organized daily schedule of activities, should help Miss Jackson to regain better control of her thoughts, impulses, and feelings.

DOCTOR JONES: I fully agree. In fact, Miss Jackson also agrees. As is so often true, the patient has a rough idea of the help needed in order to recover. Miss Jackson knows, although she could not have taken the step alone, that she must allow herself a temporary retreat from her life responsibilities. Her suffering is acute, and, as everyone has pointed out, she well recognizes that her thinking becomes confused, her feelings erratic. When I first mentioned the need for her to enter a psychiatric hospital, she wanted to know immediately if she would have the opportunity to go on talking with someone about herself, and I assured her that her psychiatrist would see her and talk with her every day. I mention this because it is evident that Miss Jackson's eventual recovery is dependent upon her talking out what has happened to her, understanding it, and thus insuring not only her getting better but also helping her change those life patterns which get her into difficulty and which led to this episode of acute disorganization.

This is a typical episode in the work of a group of clinical diagnosticians. The reader has undoubtedly noted that psychiatric diagnostic work includes much more than just an assessment of the patient's problem. The general nature of the patient's illness may be apparent to a skilled clinician in a one-hour consultation, but to prescribe treatment he must know more than the presenting problem. He must know the duration of the illness and its effects on the patient. He also must assess the patient's motivation for change. How willing or unwilling is he to do something about the illness?

Of fundamental importance are the patient's assets and how they can be used in the treatment. His financial means determine whether he will have private care or will need to take advantage of a clinic or hospital supported by public funds. His assets include much more than his bank account, however. They include an assessment of his psychic bank account. What is the nature of his investment in life? How resilient is he under stress? How adaptive is he to change? What was the nature of his personality before he became ill? What has been the quality of his relationships with people? What is his basic intelligence and how does he use it? In short, psychiatric diagnosis includes an inventory of the patient's psychological capacities and the ways in which these can be exploited in the treatment.

An accurate diagnosis is a psychiatrist's first obligation to his patient. On the basis of it he must choose that treatment which will best influence the illness in the direction of the patient's recovery. Of these, psychotherapy is the psychiatrist's most important method; the nature of psychotherapy is discussed in the next chapter. The second most important method of treatment is psychiatric hospitalization, which may be necessary for helping some patients. In many instances, psychotherapy and hospitalization are used together.

In our times, fortunately, the indications for psychiatric hospitalization have undergone extraordinary renovation and expansion. The two classic indications for the use of the psychiatric hospital are:

1. Control of self-destructive impulses is so tenuous that the patient's life is in danger.
2. Control of homicidal impulses is so tenuous that the lives of others are in danger.

Additional indications for hospitalization include:[1]

3. Control of antisocial impulses is episodic and unpredictable, and the patient requires the structured control

by the hospital to prevent further socially destructive and self-destructive behavior.

4. The functioning of the personality is severely impaired by the presence of an acute or chronic brain disease.
5. The personality is impaired by compulsive alcoholism or drug-taking.
6. A crippling degree of anxiety is present, with signs of threatening personality disorganization.
7. An acute state of personality disorganization exists.
8. Disruption of personality functioning is persistent.
9. Personality reactions are superimposed upon physical and neurological conditions and require the rehabilitation facilities of the mental hospital.
10. Pathological social or family situations require isolation of the patient as a first step in his treatment.
11. A personality disorder severely constricts the patient's emotional contacts, and the hospital can provide him with a rich emotional environment for the growth of his personality.
12. Episodes of acute emotional disturbance occur during the course of outpatient psychotherapy or psychoanalysis which may require temporary hospital care for the patient.

Assuming that these are among the most common conditions requiring hospitalization, how is the hospital used to foster the recovery of patients suffering from such illnesses? A psychiatric hospital, like any other, has a diversified staff of physicians, nurses, psychiatric aides, occupational and recreational therapists, chaplains—all of whose work is made possible by an administrative and maintenance staff. It is correct to speak, for example, of a hundred-bed psychiatric hospital; but, in contrast to the patient in a general medical and surgical hospital, the psychiatric patient uses his bed only at night. His day is filled with prescribed encounters with the various professional personnel as an attempt is made to provide a balanced program of work and play.

Perhaps the role of the psychiatric hospital can be clarified by an example. Let us follow the hospital course of the patient discussed earlier in this chapter. Miss Jackson's daily schedule while in the hospital would be something like the following:

7:00 a.m.: Arise.

7:30 a.m.: Breakfast.

At first Miss Jackson may prefer eating in her room. Later, when she shows interest in doing so, she may go to the dining room. If she tends to delay mixing with other patients, her psychiatrist may encourage her to give up her wish to isolate herself from others. He may accomplish this by asking another patient to invite Miss Jackson to join her for breakfast.

8:30 a.m.: Gardening.

Miss Jackson, with five other patients, works in the greenhouse and gardens under the supervision of a trained "activities therapist" experienced in gardening. Since Miss Jackson's thinking is disorganized and her span of attention short, the therapist begins by asking her simply to help gather flowers for the dining-room bouquets. If she falters at this task, the therapist will encourage her to return to her work. If she is indecisive about which flowers to pick, the therapist may direct the patient by saying, "Let's pick the yellow jonquils in this patch."

After a few days the complexity of the task may be

enlarged to cutting the flowers or to helping arrange the bouquets. The therapist may even point out a shelf of books on flower arrangement. Having been told something of the patient's illness by the physician, the therapist will not expect Miss Jackson to read these books at first. He will be content to have aroused a little interest in flower arrangement, and later on, as the patient's thinking becomes better organized, she may be encouraged to read the books.

As the patient improves, she may also be given tasks that may be less immediately rewarding, such as weeding a flower bed, planting seeds, watering a garden. She will also be encouraged to work with some of the other patients on a gardening project. The therapist, of course, knows that the patient's hospitalization is meant to be only a brief episode in her life. But if the patient shows interest and ability in gardening, he may draw her into discussions of how she might improve her flower beds at home or join a gardening club after returning there. As a result of this, her physician may note with pleasure Miss Jackson's remarks a week or two later: "Doctor Moore, when I go home I'm going to organize a garden club. I've been thinking about how much I've learned here, and it would be fun to see if some of us could make our home town more of a garden center."

10:30 a.m.: Art.

Miss Jackson protests to her psychiatrist, when he assigns her to an art class, "Oh, Doctor, that's one thing I can't do. I don't know a thing about art. Why, I can't even draw a straight line." Doctor Moore may suggest that since she knows so little about art this may be just the time to learn something about it. However he may manage it, Miss Jackson ends up in the art shop. Again, an activities therapist, who is trained in art, tries to engage the patient's interest. His efforts may progress quite slowly. At first he may encourage the patient to look at some reproductions of classical paintings—nothing more. But he waits for the moment when he can go further. One day Miss Jackson says to him: "Why does El Greco paint his figures in this elongated way? Did he lose his vision or something? His earlier paintings are not at all like these later ones." The therapist is pleased that some curiosity has been aroused. He answers Miss Jackson's question. He may think it appropriate now to suggest that she try her own hand at some sketching. Later, as her confidence and interest grow, he may suggest that she try a still-life in oils. Perhaps, as with the gardening, some of the activities that are used to help Miss Jackson get well may carry over as hobbies after she goes home.

Noon: Lunch.

1:00 p.m.: Discussion club.

With a number of other patients and a staff leader, Miss Jackson joins a discussion group on current events. She had stopped reading the newspapers—one small sign of her illness; now she is encouraged to resume this reading. Her illness is evident in the discussion club, for she manifests her old preoccupation with crime. It may happen that it will not be her physician who helps Miss Jackson give up this symptom; it may be another patient. One day an irritated member of the group criticizes Miss Jackson during the discussion: "I get bored with your constant talking about all the bad things that happen in the world. There are other things in the newspaper to talk about." Thus Miss Jackson, who wishes to be accepted, begins to suppress her distorted interest and to replace it with healthier ones.

2:00 p.m.: Patients' magazine.

When Doctor Moore learns that Miss Jackson likes to write, he suggests that she help the other patients who periodically put out a magazine of articles and stories written by themselves. Miss Jackson takes quickly to this idea—and promptly writes an editorial in which she castigates all news publishers as being responsible for mental illness: "The trash you publish drives people crazy!" But gradually, after discussions with her doctor and with the staff group leader who works with the patients on their magazine, Miss Jackson begins to write a children's story about a rabbit who was so scared that he stuttered.

3:00 p.m.: Recreation.

Although Miss Jackson has not engaged in any sports for years, her physician learns that she once was on her college tennis team. Again, he moves slowly. Miss Jackson gradually moves from passive participation as a spectator of the other patients' sports activities to a more active participation, and begins once more to enjoy having a tennis racket in her hand.

5:00 p.m.: Relaxation in her room.

Shortly after her admission, during this free period before dinner, Miss Jackson told one of the nurses that she admired her hair styling. The nurse suggested that, if Miss Jackson would like, she would help her arrange her hair that way the next evening. But the nurse had acted too quickly. Miss Jackson withdrew and made up a number of excuses for not keeping the appointment. But several weeks later, when Miss Jackson's recovery was more apparent, she said to the same nurse, "Say, you promised to fix my hair. When can we do it?" That evening the nurse found time to help Miss Jackson style her hair.

It is to be noted that the nurse first responded to Miss Jackson's question about her hair style by offering to help her change her own. But Miss Jackson withdrew from the offer. The competence of the psychiatric nurse is evident in the fact that she did not pursue Miss Jackson, recognizing that there was something about the patient's problem that made it impossible for her to accept this womanly gesture of help. Being a skilled nurse, she suspected that Miss Jackson was working out some of her problems through this patient-nurse relationship. She was right in her hunch. With her psychotherapist Miss Jackson was talking about how she disliked this pretty young nurse. Many of her conflicts about her own femininity were experienced and discussed in the context of a highly competitive relationship with the young nurse. Several weeks later, when the patient again approached her, the nurse knew that some conflicts were being resolved and that this overture of friendship meant that Miss Jackson had not just changed her mind about having her hair fixed, but was also changing her concept of herself.

6:00 p.m.: Dinner.

7:30 p.m.: Television, bridge, lectures, movies, parties, etc.

10:00 p.m.: Retire.

Throughout her day Miss Jackson has talked with many of the professional staff. For, besides the scheduled hours when she was under the direction of the activities therapists, she has had many other encounters with psychiatric nurses and aides. Often these encounters are informal, but they form an important part of the hospital treatment. The staff members have been informed by Miss Jackson's physician of the nature of her illness, and are trained to adapt their work to the patient's needs. In her many discussions with nurses, activity therapists, and aides, as well as with her physician, the patient is encouraged to more realistic thinking and more satisfying activities. Whenever she falters, members of the staff are at hand with words of support, clarification, help. The religious needs of the patient are also met by the hospital chaplain, and opportunities for religious services are made available. If the patient's illness is expressed as religious conflict, the chaplain can be of great assistance in helping her.

We hope that this description of the program planned for Miss Jackson conveys something of the nature of what is called "milieu treatment." It is based on a model that can be used for all patients in a psychiatric hospital. In contrast to a person like Miss Jackson, the healthy adult is able to be responsible for himself in meeting his own needs and those of others. This autonomous functioning is lost to varying degrees as a part of the personality disorganization that characterizes mental illness. When a person is referred into a psychiatric hospital, it is because someone—not always a psychiatrist; sometimes it is the patient himself—has realized that the patient temporarily needs help regulating his own life. On his admission to the hospital the staff must decide to what degree the patient can function autonomously and also to what degree they must temporarily take over the patient's responsibility for himself. Accurate assessment is of utmost importance so that the patient does exactly as much autonomous functioning as he can personally manage.

Deciding the degree of the patient's ability to function on his own is difficult. It may be even more difficult to know when and how to change the prescription as the patient demonstrates that he is ready to take more responsibility for himself. Proper *timing* is crucial. The physician, the nurses, activities therapists, and aides must do their best to avoid the extremes of either rushing the patient into situations for which he is not yet ready or hindering him from assuming responsibility he is prepared to take. A suggestion can easily be mistimed, and the staff member will have to backtrack. In our description of Miss Jackson's treatment program, we tried to indicate the importance of timing by pointing out the various "mays" or "mights" confronting the therapists.

From the moment of admission, planning is initiated for the patient's return to an independent life outside the hospital. The program of treatment itself is a series of graded efforts for developing this self-responsibility. A model for viewing this concept of psychiatric treatment can be demonstrated in the following diagram.

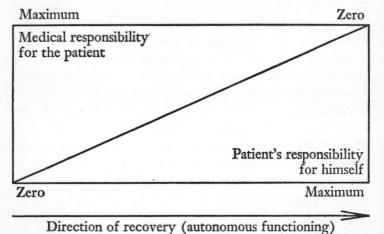

Direction of recovery (autonomous functioning)

Let us consider a patient totally incapable of taking any responsibility for himself—a patient admitted to the hospital as an emergency following an attempted suicide with barbiturates. The patient is in coma. For the moment, medical and nursing responsibility is complete; the patient's self-responsibility is nil. The staff may have to breathe for the patient. They have to remove as much of the offending chemical as possible and give an antidote to counteract the rest. They may have to feed the patient through one of his veins. They must insure the patient's metabolic and excretory functioning until he regains consciousness and can take over these functions again for himself.

When he becomes conscious again, the patient may not be grateful to those who saved his life, and his wish to die may persist, perhaps in a disguised form. If so, he must be watched twenty-four hours a day in an environment where he is protected from himself. Meanwhile, his psychiatrist will work with him to try to understand why he wishes to die. He will be given a program of daily activities prescribed specifically to help him to externalize the aggression which threatens to destroy him. He will be protected from himself until he no longer needs that protection.

Hospitalization can be prescribed like any other medicine. It can be provided in large doses or minimum doses and in titered doses in between. As the patient gradually takes over more responsibility for control of his destructive wishes and finds an external expression for them, he may cease to require the guarded care of the closed ward and move to an open service, or to a halfway house, or to a foster home, or perhaps directly to outpatient status. The patient may continue to see a psychiatrist, who will encourage and help him to understand what happened, and how it happened, and thus attempt to prevent its recurrence.

Few patients begin their psychiatric hospitalization so dramatically, and very few require so much medical responsibility. In the earlier diagram on page 86, autonomous functioning is synonymous with recovery. As the patient's self-responsibility increases, the medical responsibility decreases. Such a formulation necessarily has limitations, but to demonstrate the use of the hospital in psychiatric treatment this practical concept may be helpful. We have stressed the importance of the psychiatric-hospital environment in the treatment of the mentally ill. Later we will stress even more the importance of psychotherapy.

This description of "milieu treatment" in a psychiatric hospital may come as a surprise to many readers. For in the minds of many—all too many—the words "psychiatric-hospital treatment" conjure up a different image—an image of electro-shock, a heavy dosage of drugs, or some other kind of physical intervention. Unfortunately, these physical methods are sometimes used as if they constituted the only form of psychiatric treatment. The reader should be alerted to the fact that our description of the diagnostic study and the treatment program for Miss Jackson illustrate a high level of psychiatric practice. This level can hardly be met in an understaffed hospital. As we have repeatedly stated, good psychiatric treatment takes skilled personnel and time. As long as there is a shortage of personnel in the mental-health professions, the temptation will loom large to seek short-cut methods, especially through the use of physical treatments. Hence, every method of physical treatment that has been developed has been popularly hailed as a panacea, and has progressed through periods of overuse, often of misuse, and gradually of disuse.

Thus, when insulin-coma therapy was developed, it had a great international vogue. Its development was based on the observation that mentally ill patients who also had epilepsy sometimes got better after an epileptic seizure. Similar seizures or comas were induced in other patients by giving large doses of insulin. In some cases this treatment did have a dramatic effect. But the wild claims made for the success of insulin therapy did not hold up. There are so many potential complications in its use that it is gradually being abandoned.

A refinement of this procedure came with the discovery that such comas could be induced in a safer way by passing a mild electrical current through the brain. This electro-convulsive therapy also spread widely, because it did help some people. But, like insulin therapy, electro-shock has failed to live up to its exaggerated reputation, and its use has markedly decreased. In most good psychiatric centers today, electro-shock is used only for patients suffering from severe depressions.

Another method that created quite a stir was lobotomy. Some physicians had come to believe that by cutting certain fiber tracts in the frontal lobes of the brain the patient could be relieved of his mental suffering. This radical procedure never became as widespread as electro-shock. Some patients benefited from lobotomy, but again the wilder claims of wider success have diminished, and the idea of lobotomy as a cure for mental illness is now pretty much relegated to the pages of medical history.

Today drugs are popular. The newly developed synthetic drugs, both the tranquilizers and the energizers, are a part of the physician's armamentarium. But in the opinion of many psychiatrists and other physicians they are frequently overused and the claims made for their effectiveness are exaggerated. While the drugs are useful, they must be prescribed with care. They are not a magic solution to treating the mentally ill.

There is no magic short-cut to successful treatment of mental illness. Patients get well through other people. They improve through their daily association with people who are concerned about them and are trained to treat them. Any physical treatment method has but one purpose: to bring the patient to the point where he can make use of the people who are available to him—that is, to prepare the patient for "people treatment." Psychiatry has not found a drug that can substitute for human interchange in helping a patient to find for himself a better way of living.

Dr. George H. Preston has stated this thesis forcefully:

> No building ever cured a patient. Neither medicine, psychiatry, hydrotherapy, occupational therapy, dietetics, drugs, electricity, music, dramatics, surgery, psychoanalysis, religion nor psychiatric social work ever cured a patient. Recoveries occur only when such techniques are applied directly and continuously to individual patients by trained people. People, not things, or theories, cure patients.[2]

6

Psychiatric Practice —Psychotherapy

When anyone goes to a physician, he expects him to find out what is wrong and to treat it. Most people anticipate that to relieve suffering the physician will have to *do something* to the patient—make a physical examination, prescribe some medication, or perform surgery. Of course, the physician does much more than prescribe pills or percuss the chest—he listens, he counsels, he advises, he educates, he comforts. But the wise old horse-and-buggy doctor knew that words were not enough. He recognized that patients came to him expecting that something physical would be done to them, and that his failure to respond to that expectation might leave the patients doubtful that he knew what he was doing. Therefore, he would often prescribe a medicine as innocuous as sugar; it met the patient's expectations, and often such "drugs" did help. The patient felt confident that his doctor knew what he was doing; and, because something tangible was being done for him, he began to feel better.

Traditionally physicians have attempted to treat both mental and physical illness by doing something physical to the patient. But this tradition only led to stagnation for psychiatry because most mental illness does not have a physical etiology. Mental illness usually is caused not by microbes but by psychological conflicts. Thus the therapeutic nihilism that was the shadow of psychiatry for centuries had a basis in reality—the lack of available treatment methods reinforced the medical attitude that mental illness is irreversible. The result was that the therapeutic nihilism surrounding the mentally ill had the durability and strength of steel.

It was in this climate that psychotherapy, as it is now professionally practiced, had its beginning. Sigmund Freud, not knowing what to do for the mentally ill patients who sought his help and dissatisfied with the then current methods for treating them, began doing something that at first seems very simple. One wonders, in fact, why it was not until the late nineteenth century that it happened. Freud did with the mentally ill what physicians have always had to do with their patients—he listened to their complaints.

But Freud did do something different. He began to listen to psychiatric patients, not just for a few minutes but for a number of hours. And, as the patient talked, something began to happen. First of all, the patient found that with an unhurried listener he had plenty to talk about. Some of this included memories of feelings and events from the past, and every now and then, as the patient talked about some of his past experiences, the recall was associated with a great deal of feeling. But even this was not the surprising feature of these early "experiments" of Freud. The surprise was that the patient began to get better; his symptoms began to change and to disappear. Freud was pleased to see his patients improve, but fortunately for mankind he was the kind of scientist who is driven to understand *how* the improvement came about. He dedicated the rest of his life to trying to understand and elaborate his early observations and to check them against subsequent clinical experiences.

Freud was not the first to discover that talking over one's problems with someone else often makes one feel better. But he did first discover that, if the physician persists in his professional listening to and talking with a mentally ill person, he can understand and help the patient. This discovery was to revolutionize psychiatry. But even that was not Freud's greatest contribution to mankind. His new approach and new theories introduced for the first time in the history of man a new companion for the mentally ill—*hope*. For, implicit in Freud's new approach was a scientifically based optimism—*the behavior of the mentally ill can be understood and can be changed*.

But it took a long time before more than a few physicians took Freud seriously. Few read his books—first-edition copies now worth hundreds of dollars remained unopened on the storage shelves of the publisher. Men and women of the Victorian era tittered in private about this strange doctor who wrote about sex. Physicians acted as if man did not have a sexual drive; medical textbooks of the time included no reference to it. Perhaps the human family's first experience of the tragedy of world war in the teens of the twentieth century frightened man into reading Freud. For this "sex doctor" was also writing about other things—particularly about man's destructiveness. Appalled by the wholesale bloodshed during World War I, man could well be frightened by his undeniable capacity to destroy.

Out of Freud's work came the present-day concept of professional psychotherapy. It is not correct to say that Freud discovered psychotherapy; in fact, he seldom used the word. The method of treatment that he developed he called psychoanalysis. But Freud laid the groundwork for all forms of "talking treatment"—that is, treatment in which, with the help of the therapist, the patient talks out his problem. Today psychotherapy is the generic term used to describe all "talking treatment," of which psychoanalysis is but one specialized form.

A central problem in trying to understand the nature of medical psychotherapy is first to differentiate it from the many other everyday human interactions which, as a matter of fact, may have "therapeutic" side effects. For example, many Catholics undoubtedly experience a therapeutic effect from going to confession. Does this make the confessor a psychotherapist? And does this mean, as some have said, that the confessional is a substitute for psychotherapy for Catholics?

And how can we differentiate psychotherapy from the kind of help that is derived from everyday talking with others? When Mrs. Anderson stops in for a cup of coffee with her neighbor, Mrs. Blum, her conversation drifts eventually to a discussion of the problem the Andersons are having with their daughter Sally. Somehow or other the conversation gives Mrs. Anderson some assurance about how to handle the problem; and later that day, when she brings herself to talking with Sally, the problem reaches a satisfactory solution. Both Mrs. Anderson and Sally benefited from the morning *Kaffeeklatsch*. Are we to conclude that Mrs. Blum did "psychotherapy"? She may never have heard the word. But the fact is that her conversation with Mrs. Anderson did have a "therapeutic" effect.

On a different level, what would we say of the nun who gives career guidance to one of her high-school students, or the priest who helps one of his young parishioners through some personal difficulties, or the confessor who gives spiritual guidance and direction? Are these people doing psychotherapy?

Before attempting to answer these questions, it is important to recognize that only a fraction of the total human sicknesses—physical or mental—are treated by physicians. In fact, many physical and mental aberrations which might be called sickness by a physician are called something else by other people. The disturbance may become known officially as sickness only when the physician so labels it. Certainly many who are suffering from mental illnesses are being "treated" by people other than psychiatrists, and the "physicians" in these instances may not even be aware of the "patient's illness" or their "therapeutic" role with the individual.

One is reminded of the man who was left an orphan at an early age and was reared by unconcerned relatives who did not want him. He slowly developed a severe mental illness, and as an adult wandered aimlessly from one job to another and from one city to another. He had no home—no one wanted him—and his illness so crippled his emotional life that he found it increasingly difficult to reach out to anyone. One day he talked with a priest, who asked him if he had ever thought of being a religious brother. Despite his serious psychopathology the man appeared on the surface only as an overly shy, quiet, seclusive person. When he applied for the religious community he was accepted as a brother. His abbot became the first consistent "father" he had ever known and the other monks accepted him as a member of their religious family. This new life helped to make up for some of the deprivations of his early life. He did extremely well and labored until his death in God's service. He never saw a psychiatrist. No one except the community's physician and the brother's confessor ever knew the full story of this man's mental suffering. The priest who counseled him and suggested the religious life to him certainly did not think he was doing therapy. And we can be quite certain that the abbot never thought of himself as supervising a treatment program for this brother. And, yet, the "treatment program" had a good therapeutic result—a result that possibly surpassed what a psychiatrist might have achieved.

Let us return to a consideration of how efforts to help people by listening and talking to them differ and how they are similar. Several criteria are implicit in any helping situation:

1. The intent of the person seeking help (patient, penitent, student, parishioner).
2. The intent of the helper (psychotherapist, confessor, teacher, pastor, religious counselor).
3. The nature of the "contract" between the helper and the person seeking help (treatment, confession, counseling).
4. The skills and training of the helper.
5. The nature of the problem.

Let us consider several anecdotal accounts of one person who is helped by another, and apply the above criteria to these examples from everyday life.

CASE I

A twenty-two-year-old man tells a priest in the confessional about his severe scruples. The priest tries to help his penitent with spiritual guidance. He advises the penitent to have a regular confessor. Using the same kind of spiritual counseling that he has used to benefit other scrupulous penitents, the priest notes that this man's problem remains unchanged after several months. He recognizes that the problem, which appears to be spiritual, is most likely an emotional one. He may discuss this opinion openly with the penitent and suggest that he seek the advice of a psychiatrist. (It is to be noted that psychiatrists are seeing an increasing number of people referred directly from the confessional.)

But how do the five criteria implicit in any helping situation apply to this account? The young penitent went to the priest with the intent of making a good confession and obtaining spiritual guidance. The priest's intent was to give sacramental absolution and to offer indicated spiritual counsel. The understood "contract" between them was the age-old one implicit between penitent and confessor, based on Christ's commissioning his priests to forgive sin in His name. The penitent did not go to the confessional to get "treatment," nor did the confessor think of himself as a therapist, even though he may have used skills which are similar to those of a professional psychotherapist. He plied his skills as a priest in giving absolution and in offering counsel. But when he began to suspect a deeper underlying problem he suggested to the penitent that perhaps some emotional difficulty was tied up in the spiritual problem for which he had come to the confessional for help. Therefore the priest shifted his original intent; his goal now was to bring his penitent to seek the needed psychiatric help. In so doing he had to help the penitent shift his goal from going to confession to seeking medical help for an emotional illness.

CASE II

A young lady comes to her high-school teacher, Sister Scholastica, for help in planning her career. The student tells Sister that she thinks she would like to study medicine. Sister Scholastica outlines the academic progression required to obtain a degree as Doctor of Medicine and talks with the student about various colleges. But she does much more than that. She reflects with the student about how serious her motivation is for a medical career. She may remind the student of her difficulty with chemistry in high school and tell her that chemistry courses will therefore require extra effort. She will undoubtedly also talk about reconciling a medical career with the job of being a wife and mother. Sister may even suggest that she talk with a local woman physician, mother of four children, who Sister knows has made a success at both careers.

In the course of this counseling Sister Scholastica has a decisive effect on this young student. She uses some of the skills of a psychotherapist, but again, if we consider the criteria listed earlier to differentiate various helping situations, the difference is even more apparent. The student comes with the intent of learning more about a career, and Sister responds with the intent of helping the girl with her career by counseling her. The goals of the counseling experience are thus explicit in the minds of both, as is the nature of the implied contract between them. The student comes not with an emotional problem but with a career problem, and the skills used by Sister are those of an able educational and career counselor.

CASE III

John and Mary Minter have been married seven years and have two children. When they were married they were deeply in love, but in the last two years their life together has become a living hell for Mary. John has lost three jobs in these two years because of excessive drinking. The loss of income has severely reduced their standard of living, increased marital strife has developed, and Mary has become exhausted in her efforts to protect the children from John's drunken behavior. Mary is a proud woman, and for a long time she has told no one about what was really going on. Finally, in a moment of exhaustion, she calls and asks to see her parish priest, Father Brown. All that she has kept to herself for so long floods out with many tears. Father Brown has two jobs—first, to support Mary in her time of difficulty, and also to help Mary get John to the medical help he needs. After talking for some time, he tells Mary that her husband will have to have help. Mary protests, saying that maybe if she would just try harder she could help John solve his problem. Father Brown asks her if she thinks she could do any more to help him than she has been doing for over two years. He suggests that it is about time for her to face the fact that John has a serious sickness. Father Brown has an extremely difficult task, first in convincing Mary that John is ill, and second in getting John to go for help. He may succeed in getting John to talk with their family physician, and perhaps the priest and the physician, working together, can get him into a psychiatric hospital.

Mary has come to a crisis and reaches for help. It is unfortunate that her cry for help could not be made until the problem had overwhelmed her. She turns to her parish priest; she takes the problem not to the confessional but to the rectory. Her intent is to get help. Father Brown does not have a penitent, but he has a parishioner who is sick at heart and in trouble with a complicated situation. He "treats" Mary by letting her talk out her problem, encouraging her to unload her heartache in tears. Then he begins to talk with Mary about the cause of her troubles, helping her to accept the fact that her husband is seriously ill.

In this example Mary seeks guidance for dealing with a difficult situation. Father Brown has to help Mary cope with her personal tragedy and extend his efforts to try to get the psychiatric help John needs. Mary does not come with a specific spiritual problem, but is desperate about a husband who is ill. Her intent is less clear, for at first she does not wish to accept the fact that her husband is ill or needs help. Father Brown's task is complicated—how to help two of his parishioners who are in difficulty. During the course of his efforts he has to clarify Mary's intent and help mobilize her husband's wish for help. The contract between Mary and her parish priest is less defined at the outset; Father Brown has to make it explicit. The problem is serious, and Father Brown may well feel that he has to stretch his skills in pastoral counseling to get John to treatment.

Let us now apply the original five criteria to professional psychotherapy. The intent of the person seeking help is usually apparent—relief from psychic discomfort—and the intent of the psychotherapist is equally apparent—to try to help the patient by sitting with him, listening and talking to him. The implicit contract between the patient and the psychotherapist is made explicit by the psychotherapist. The therapist agrees to see the patient for regular appointments at a varying frequency (one to five times per week), for an agreed period of time (twenty to fifty minutes), and until the treatment is terminated by mutual agreement of the patient and the therapist. The therapist commits these regular hours in his schedule for this patient and will not use them for others except in an emergency. Therefore, part of the contract includes the patient's agreement to the condition that if he misses appointments without previous arrangement he will be charged for the time. A fee per hour is agreed upon and the patient is expected, as a part of the contract, to pay for the treatment. The patient assumes that the therapist has, through training and experience, mastered those skills required for treating his problem. The therapist accepts the patient for treatment only after determining through a diagnostic examination that the patient's problem is amenable to psychotherapy.

Most people think of psychotherapy as a very mysterious process. Even the patient who is about to begin psychotherapy brings misconceptions about what is going to happen. A typical attitude is reflected in the patient who says, "Okay, I'm here. Now tell me how I can lead a happier life and get rid of these annoying symptoms." Dr. Ernst Ticho, commenting on the patient's perception of treatment, states: "There are many patients who see therapy as an end, and not as a means to achieve an end. The therapy becomes a goal in itself, instead of an instrument for achieving a goal and for enlarging one's goals." [1]

The patient who comes with expectations of quick magic solutions must learn that the basis of psychotherapy is reflection. He learns to examine his behavior in the past as well as in the present. Gradually he comes to learn that even his most bizarre symptom has causes which can be understood and changed. The patient also, sometimes to his surprise, finds solutions for his problems within himself and not from advice given by the therapist. If the patient comes with the expectation that the therapist will help him by telling him what to do, the psychotherapy may well begin with the patient's being encouraged to reflect about this expectation.

For example, a therapist might comment, "How is it that you are looking for someone to tell you what to do with your life?"

Psychiatrists are often misunderstood about an attitude which they must have toward their patients' behavior. Curiously enough, this attitude is contrary to human tendency and has to be cultivated as part of clinical training. In order to be helpful the psychiatrist must have an attitude of non-judgmental concern for human suffering. But critics mistakenly deduce from this that the psychiatrist has no sense or standard of what is right or wrong. Psychiatry is just as moral as any other science; in fact, it well may be more so. And the fact that the psychiatrist does not "lecture" the prostitute who seeks his help about her lack of moral behavior does not mean that he is without a concept of health for his patient, a concept which does not include prostitution. But first he has to accept his patient as she is; what is more, the patient must feel that she is accepted. Then the psychotherapeutic work can begin. The reader may find it hard to believe, but the psychiatrist rarely sees anyone who is committing some immoral act who is not already very much aware of that fact and concerned about it. The psychiatrist cannot help by judging the patient; he helps by sympathetic concern and by beginning a search for causes which will lead the patient to an understanding of himself. He attempts to help the patient remove those conflicts that defeat the patient's wish for a satisfying life, which essentially is a moral one.

But what does transpire in the course of psychotherapy? Dr. Carl Epstein once wrote this description of the process:

Psychotherapy is the direct treatment of one person by one other person using predominantly verbal means. That is, the treatment is conducted by two persons talking together, rather than by the giving of drugs, by the use of physical measure or by other means. . . .

Communication between patient and therapist occurs not only in words. Changing qualities of the patient's voice, his changing facial expressions, changes in his posture and manner also speak volumes. Likewise, a quizzical look, perhaps a smile by the therapist, may be a more effective means of communication with the patient than words.

The essential materials of psychotherapy are not only the thoughts and ideas of the patient. Equally vital in the therapy process are his sensations, his emotions, his dreams, his reveries and phantasies. His interests and his interpersonal relationships, past and present, including his relationship with the therapist, are equally significant." [2]

But does the psychotherapist have specific techniques which he uses in talking and listening to the patient? Indeed he does, but psychotherapy involves more than technique. As Dr. Epstein indicates, psychotherapy involves skills in observation and listening; what the patient says may, for the skilled listener, take on special meanings which can be understood in the context of the dynamic forces of that patient's life. It is tempting to think that what the psychotherapist does is different because of the techniques he uses. In fact, some of them are the same ones used every day by a job foreman, a teacher, a nurse, or a politician to influence people. But the difference lies in his depth of understanding of human behavior and in his skill in the use of the psychotherapeutic techniques.

Dr. Edward Bibring has attempted a classification of these techniques. He defines technique as "any purposive, more or less typified, verbal or nonverbal behavior on the part of the therapist which intends to affect the patient in the direction of the (intermediary or final) goals of the treatment." [3] He lists five groups of basic techniques:

1. *Suggestion*—"the induction of ideas, actions, etc. . . . by the therapist (an individual in an authoritative position) in the patient (an individual in a dependent position)." The therapist uses suggestion when he points out that if the patient continues to drink excessively during the treatment he may succeed in keeping out of the treatment the very conflicts that cause the drinking, and thus defeat his intent in having psychotherapy.

2. *Abreaction.* In the use of this technique the therapist encourages the patient to remember in full detail the traumatic events from his past, so that emotional tensions surrounding them are discharged. In treating a patient whose mother had died when he was eight, the therapist encouraged the patient to recall every detail about his mother—her illness, her death, and her funeral. Many feelings of his sense of loss, his sorrow and hurt, were re-experienced in the treatment hour as he recalled these painful memories.

3. *Manipulation.* There are many techniques of manipulation, all of which attempt to influence the patient in a way that will promote the treatment. The therapist may attempt to influence the patient's commitment to the treatment by increasing the frequency of the appointments. Manipulative techniques are used less in psychotherapy than in counseling, where advice-giving, guidance, exhortation, or insistence on a course of action are commonly used. However, any tendency to attempt to direct the patient's life is contrary to the spirit of psychotherapy.

4. *Clarification.* None of the above techniques particularly increases the patient's understanding of himself. The objective of clarification is to increase it. After gaining considerable knowledge of the patient, the therapist attempts to help him "see" something about himself by formulating in a precise restatement what the patient seems to feel and think. For example, after hearing a patient discuss for several hours his difficulties in getting along with other people, the therapist might comment, "Have you noticed that in every relationship you have mentioned in recent days, you seem to expect everyone automatically to reject you, and to think little of you and of what you might have to contribute?"

5. *Interpretation.* When used in its correct technical sense, interpretation is limited to work with repressed unconscious material. When the therapist has accumulated enough evidence from what the patient tells him, and when he understands this evidence and sees in it a meaning for the patient, he will state directly to the patient that a specific unconscious process appears to determine his manifest behavior. For example, a therapist might say to a patient when the evidence indicates it, "You play the martyr to hide from yourself, and from me, and from others how angry you really are." Interpretation is *the* technique used most in an intensive reorganizing and resynthesizing therapy such as psychoanalysis. Undoubtedly, this technique requires the greatest skill to execute properly. However, it is the favorite weapon of the parlor psychologizer who will tell you at the drop of a hat that he interprets your poor bridge-playing as concrete evidence that you hated your father and preferred your mother, and therefore withdrew from ever winning at

any competition. Needless to say, such wild use of "interpretation," even on the level of a parlor game, is dangerous.

At this point it must be abundantly apparent to the reader that, with the exception of the psychotherapeutic technique of interpretation, educators, priests, lawyers, parents—in fact, all who try to be helpful to others through verbal communication—use in their own way the same techniques which the psychotherapist uses in his professional work. Because of his specific training, the professional psychotherapist will use these skills with a specialized competence and with the specific intent of helping sick people. He will use them in various combinations, depending upon the nature of the patient's problems and the goal of the treatment. As was mentioned earlier, in an ambitious psychotherapy where there is an attempted analysis and resynthesis of the patient's personality (such as in psychoanalysis), the therapist will avoid such techniques as suggestion and manipulation in order to encourage the patient's participation in the treatment, and will rely heavily upon interpretation and abreaction.

All attempts to help another through verbal communication can be projected on a continuum:

> *everyday interactions*
> *education*
> *counseling*
> *psychotherapy*
> *psychoanalysis*

Toward the middle of the continuum are the various counseling skills, and toward the top, Mrs. Blum's *Kaffeeklatsch* therapy is included. At the bottom is the most intensive and ambitious type of psychotherapy, namely psychoanalysis. The skills required to do the work increase as one moves from top to bottom on the continuum. Professional requirements for training and study are likewise a continuum from top to bottom. And within each area we can note other professional competencies. For example, not only has the pastoral counselor acquired some skill as a counselor, but most of his professional training has been in theology. To be most helpful it is important that each person recognize the area and the boundaries of his competence. A priest may be a highly competent counselor, but he will not attempt to do psychotherapy or psychoanalysis. Nor for that matter will a psychiatrist attempt to give spiritual direction. But well-trained psychotherapists have available to them, because of their long and specialized training and experience, the broadest range of skills throughout the continuum. A psychotherapist can also be expert as a psychological counselor, in addition to being qualified to treat the more serious emotional illnesses.

Psychotherapy involves highly technical skills which are not easily developed. They do not come just from reading a book or taking a semester's course in human psychology. Much time and effort enter into the making of a competent psychotherapist, time and effort spent both in professional academic training and in carefully directed clinical experience. Even an M.D. degree plus a three-year psychiatric residency does not automatically make a person an effective psychotherapist. No one realizes this more than therapists themselves, and they are therefore concerned and confounded by the present-day eagerness of so many to cast themselves into the psychotherapist's role. Psychotherapy is hard work, it is difficult, and the responsibilities that the psychotherapist assumes for the life of another human being are grave.

Since such responsibilities must not be taken lightly, professional mental-health workers see the need for protecting the public by requiring some kind of licensure of the psychotherapist. Psychiatrists who are trained in psychotherapy are, like other physicians, licensed by the state board of medicine. But psychotherapy is also done by clinical psychologists, who themselves are spearheading moves for adequate legal regulation of their professional practice. They recognize the need for providing the public with protection from malpractice by the untrained and misguided.

For the skills we are talking about lead the therapist into the deeper regions of the human personality, into the often unrecognized areas of the human psyche wherein are discerned persistent influences from one's past. These become intelligible against the background of the genetic or dynamic developmental process of the personality. An experienced psychotherapist has the skill of reading and interpreting many of the intangibles in personal relationships; also, he has the skill of fostering and using the mysterious dynamics of transference.

Today there is a prairie-fire spread of enthusiasm that is infecting all sorts of people with the desire to try to do psychotherapy under various guises. This is a dangerous trend. While no one would think of letting a person untrained in surgery remove his appendix, many are all too ready to air their psychic problems before almost anyone. The danger lies in this "anyone" attempting psychotherapy. Many a psychiatrist can tell us that meddling with the deeper aspects of the human person by an untrained "therapist" can involve greater risks than most want to recognize.

It is not a spirit of professionalism that prompts these warnings. We readily grant that psychotherapy is not necessarily restricted to the medically trained person. But it seems prudent to restrict it to a medical setting. Trained nonmedical psychotherapists usually work in conjunction with physicians.

The dangerous spread of untrained "psychotherapists" has probably been encouraged by today's emphasis on various kinds of counseling. There is, of course, a legitimate form of help called counseling, but it becomes distorted and dangerous when the counselor becomes too closely identified with psychiatry and the work of the psychotherapist. When the counselor tries to ape the trappings and technique of psychotherapy, he may be giving bad "medicine" to his client.

Priests and other religious are called upon nearly every day to do some type of counseling. Certainly such counseling should be encouraged and its skills should be developed. But the counselor should be working within the confines of his professional competence, or, better, within the scope of his own vocation. In this way our parish rectories will not be converted into clinics nor our schools into treatment centers.

At the heart of every member of the service professions is the question of his professional identity. A priest, for example, who is also an educator is certainly called on to counsel students. But this should be within the framework of his identity as a priest-teacher. He should know what a given student requires to make a career, and he should be able to direct that student spiritually and academically toward that career. His competence lies here; he is not trained (ordinarily) to delve into the deeper personality problems of a student. It is to be hoped that the priest, when confronted with these, will recognize the need for someone who is professionally trained to handle such problems. Surely the intent of a school is not to run a therapeutic center; nor is the intent of the faculty to be psychotherapists. Yet the rash of such tendencies is a present reality.

Again, there is a legitimate skill that is comprised under the term "pastoral counseling," and "the cure of souls" has a history almost as old as Christianity itself. But the emphasis must never be removed from the term "pastoral." If the theological dimension is lost sight of, there is again the dangerous tendency to play the role of the psychotherapist.

A study made by the Joint Commission for Mental Health revealed that, in the sample studied, forty-two per cent of those with personal problems who actually seek help turn first to their clergyman.[4] This means that the priest is in a strategic position to offer help within the area of his professional competence. We believe that the parishioner who first goes to his priest with emotional difficulties and problems is seeking priestly help. And if the priest remains within his religious identity, using his priestly ways of helping people, he can indeed be of assistance to a great many. One of his tasks is to assess the problem and his own resources for meeting it. In some instances the priest may come to see that the problem will not respond to his ministry. Hasty psychiatric referrals, of course, are not in order. But part of the priest's identity includes a recognition of limitations as well as skills —a recognition that is sharpened by experience. When, after trying his usual skills in helping a parishioner, the priest sees that the problem has not resolved itself, he will acknowledge the existence of a deeper emotional problem which may require the skills of a professional psychotherapist.

In our times there will not be enough trained psychotherapists to treat all the people who could benefit from their skills. This shortage often encourages the uninitiated to try their hand at "psychotherapy." Some such efforts are sincere, and one cannot quarrel with the fact that practical realities may demand that many of the service professions stretch their counseling skills to try to help sick people.

Psychiatrists are very much concerned about the need to prepare an increased number of mental-health workers in psychotherapy. After a physician completes medical school and one year of internship, he can begin specializing in psychiatry, which requires three more years. He may combine this with training in an institute of psychoanalysis and prepare himself as a psychoanalyst, which will require several more years after he completes his psychiatric residency. Much of the professional education of the physician in medical school is not used by him later as a psychotherapist. This is abundantly apparent in the fact that clinical psychologists can be trained after they have completed their Ph.D. degree to become excellent psychotherapists; and some complete psychoanalytic training. Interested mental-health personnel are at present studying the education of the psychotherapist with the hope that in the future we may see the development of a new type of educational program that prepares mental-health personnel specifically in the art and science of psychotherapy.

7

The Psychiatric Referral

The reader will recall from our Introduction the letter from the nun in Dubuque who wrote to a psychiatrist for advice about her so-called "lazy student." The sister felt great concern for this lad, who in her opinion was one of the brightest students in her class, yet was failing in his grades. Her concern would, of course, be shared by the psychiatrist. But just what response should he give, what suggestions should he offer? Should the sister refer this student to a psychiatrist? If so, how should she go about it? It is to these questions that we now turn.

Assuming the accuracy of the sister's observation that the student is in no way mentally handicapped, one would immediately ask why it is that this boy is failing to harness and develop his intellectual capacities. The psychiatrist would suspect that this student is failing because of emotional difficulties which so preoccupy him that his scholastic endeavors suffer. Further, the psychiatrist would suspect that the student is struggling with some of the disturbing aspects of change from one phase of life to another—in this case, adolescence. From the frustrated tone of the sister's letter, it was clear that she was confronted with a problem that was beyond her ordinary resources for dealing with students. The psychiatrist assumes that the boy's problem is not mysterious and need not be endured with resignation. Lacking other indications of more complicated emotional problems, he might well assume that even a few hours of talking with this young man may decisively help him reverse his poor school performance.

We recall that this sister felt that a referral to a psychiatrist seemed called for in this case, but she was not certain that the principal of the school would agree to this. Also, she anticipated that the boy's parents would be outraged by the suggestion that there is "something wrong with our boy." Assuming that there is a psychiatrist available to whom the student could be referred, what are some of the problems that the sister faces?

Probably many a teacher has had the experience of being the target of an angry barrage from parents at the mere suggestion that their child needs psychiatric help. Undoubtedly there is a real temptation to shut one's eyes to some problem children rather than face such a barrage. "I simply cannot afford the turmoil that such a referral kicks up. It isn't worth the price. The parents get mad; the students get disturbed; the principal is annoyed at my rocking the boat. I know this isn't the right attitude, but referring a student to a psychiatrist can be a major undertaking. It's looked upon as a last-ditch measure, and there's no simple way to do it." This might well mirror the thoughts of many teachers.

As a matter of fact, referral is not a simple thing, but neither is it something that has to be impossibly complicated. When confronted with such a situation as, for example, the "lazy student" who does not respond to ordinary teaching efforts, we would expect the teacher to accumulate all the evidence that leads her to suspect something is wrong. This evidence should be discussed with the principal, and in the end the principal should be the one who talks to the boy's parents. Perhaps some intermediary modes of help may be sought: the student counselor or the chaplain. Their inability to get to the bottom of the boy's problem would suggest to the principal the advisability of a psychiatric referral.

The principal's interview with the parents will require skill. Obviously, to blurt out awkwardly the recommendation that the boy should see a psychiatrist will provoke nothing but resistance to the idea. But an experienced principal knows that a youngster's emotional troubles are not limited to one area of his life. The parents may not readily admit it, but if their boy is doing poorly in school because of emotional problems, these same problems are showing up at home, too. The principal should keep in mind that the parents want to do what is right by their child; but to be told that there is something wrong with him smacks somewhat of saying that they have failed. We can expect them to react by denying such failures and projecting blame onto someone or something else. Hence, one of the principal's tasks is to help the parents see that perhaps no one has failed, but rather that the child is having some troubles that may require special help.

Thus, once all the evidence about the student's failure is collected, and with a clear grasp of the classroom situation including the teacher's varied efforts to help the student, the principal arranges a meeting with the student's parents. That interview might progress as follows:

PRINCIPAL: I'm certain that you are wondering why I asked to talk with you.

MOTHER: Yes, we have worried that something might be wrong.

DAD: Is Johnny in some kind of trouble?

PRINCIPAL: No—at least not the kind of trouble you mean. Johnny hasn't done anything wrong. But I have been concerned, and so has his teacher, about his poor marks.

MOTHER: Well, Johnny has been very busy since he went out for basketball. As soon as the season is over he'll have more time to study.

PRINCIPAL: Perhaps, but does he use the time he does have at home to study?

MOTHER: Yes, he does. But, you know, I have wondered about that new teacher he has. I don't like to say anything about a nun, but Sister Ann is just not the teacher Sister Cecilia was, that's for sure. Johnny didn't have this kind of trouble before.

DAD: Johnny isn't as interested in his school work as he was. I feel sure it's because of that new sister. Maybe she just isn't a good teacher.

PRINCIPAL: Sister Ann is an excellent teacher, and most of her students are doing quite well. I guess you feel that someone is at fault or has done wrong by Johnny. But I have to tell you, I think the trouble is with Johnny.

MOTHER: What do you mean? What sort of trouble?

DAD: Johnny's never been in any trouble!

PRINCIPAL: You know, growing up isn't always easy. I keep wondering if Johnny isn't perhaps worried about something—something about himself—and is so tied up with that, that his studies are suffering.

DAD: Well, if something were wrong with our boy, he'd tell us—he's always done so in the past.

PRINCIPAL: Most of us start out telling our parents everything, but when we get to be adolescents, we may find it difficult to talk as openly as before. It's part of growing up to want to be more and more independent, to do it all on our own. And some of the worries become so personal and involved that we tend to lock them up inside ourselves.

MOTHER: Oh, I think you're just trying to cover up for a poor teacher! Why, I've never heard such talk before. Our Johnny doesn't have a bit of trouble anywhere except right here in your school. He is not a bit different at home than he ever was. (Then, losing control, the mother bursts into tears.)

PRINCIPAL (after waiting a moment): I wish you were right. I wish it were just something wrong here at school; then I could do something about it. But I want you to know that I have studied Johnny's difficulties very carefully and have spent a good deal of time talking with his teacher, who is just as concerned as I am. Johnny is having psychological difficulties—difficulties inside himself that he doesn't understand—and they are showing up here at school. Despite the fact that he is obviously very bright, his grades have gone way down. And I feel that these psychological difficulties are showing up elsewhere in his life. I think you know this, too, and maybe you are frightened by some of the things you have observed about your son, but you reassure yourselves that he will be all right tomorrow. You see, no boy has such troubles only at school, and Johnny is most likely showing his inner troubles to you at home, too. (Long, patient pause.)

MOTHER (reluctantly): Well, he has been awfully touchy lately. I said something to him just last night—it didn't amount to anything—oh, I remember, I asked him to get the evening paper for his dad. He had just come in from school; he slammed down his books, banged the screen door, got the paper; then he went to his room and shut the door. He didn't used to act that way.

PRINCIPAL: Johnny has always been very popular with the other students. Have you noticed any change in that?

DAD: Come to think of it, he does seem to spend more time at home alone lately.

MOTHER: Yes, that's right. He seems like he's always got something on his mind, like he doesn't pay any attention to what is going on around him.

PRINCIPAL: Johnny may need someone to help him right now. He probably needs to talk to someone, and it seems he can't get the help he needs from you folks or from me.

MOTHER: But what can we do?

PRINCIPAL: I'm not certain. But I would encourage you to consider the possibility that Johnny may need some special help. You might want to talk this over with your family doctor. You know, every situation is different, and I don't feel confident enough to say that you should immediately consult a psychiatrist or a mental-health clinic. Lots of children run into snags as they grow up, and they need help; your son isn't the only one. With other students I have had, their family physician has often felt that now is the time to seek the help of a mental-health expert with problems that seem to defy our own efforts, rather than run the risk of the boy's developing further dif- ficulties. Right now there is nothing seriously wrong in Johnny's life. We know he is an able student because of his past performance. The question I think you have to decide is whether you want to do something now that may help insure Johnny's growing out of these temporary difficulties.

DAD: You don't think he is mentally ill, do you?

PRINCIPAL: You know, mental illness is hard to define. The word implies to you that your son is crazy. But that's not so. Mental illness is a much broader notion, and people today don't wait until really serious illness develops before they see a psychiatrist. More and more people seek help early, rather than wait until they are completely worn out physically and psychologically from fighting an emotional problem. With Johnny, the question now is do we need to do something to prevent serious complications from developing.

DAD: Well, that's a relief. We surely appreciate your asking us to come in and talk this over. Johnny is very important to us. And, as you said, I guess we expected him to just grow out of this problem overnight. Mother, don't you think we should make an appointment and talk this over with Doctor Dunne?

MOTHER: Yes, I do. Doctor Dunne has taken care of Johnny since he was a baby. He'll probably be as surprised as we are about these changes in Johnny, but I am confident he'll be able to tell us what to do.

This anecdotal account may help demonstrate how frightened parents may require the support of their child's school principal as a necessary first step before psychiatric referral can be made. It may demonstrate also how a religious educator remains in his own role and simply acquaints the student's parents with the faculty's observations of their boy and suggests that they may wish to discuss these observations with a physician who can better advise them about the possible need for psychiatric attention. This material also demonstrates the need for presenting such a recommendation in a carefully planned way. Note that we are suggesting that it is the principal, not the teacher, who should make this recommendation to the parents. In this way the teacher can more smoothly continue her work with the student in the classroom.

What we do *not* wish to imply from this material is that every student who is doing inadequate work is in need of a psychiatrist. There is always the danger of a kind of overconcern, the danger of quickly referring every problem case to a psychiatrist. At the same time, many priests and nuns do want to know just when and how a psychiatric referral should be made. Concern is generated in the minds of many who feel that if they only knew more about the technical aspects of psychiatry they would be able to make more and more referrals. We would like to take a stand against such thinking.

Our plea here is for a steady reliance on common sense. After all, gross signs of mental illness—delusions (fixed false beliefs), hallucinations (hearing, seeing, or feeling objects that are not there), sudden behavioral changes, and the like—are easily recognized by nearly everyone. Nor is there any great difficulty in getting medical help for such cases. But these are the least common manifestations of mental illness. As we saw in Chapter 3, our present-day concept of mental illness is much broader. Temporary failures in adjustment are part of everyday life and represent temporary episodes of "mental illness." But the human personality is extremely resourceful and is quite capable of handling most of these transitory episodes. And, even if our own recuperative powers are not sufficient, we most likely will reach out to someone else for help, hardly recognizing that we are doing so. We have all experienced talking over our problems with a friend, a teacher, a priest, and often enough just talking out our problem with a sympathetic listener is adequate "therapy."

The sister who wrote about her "lazy student" was an excellent observer. She noted that her observations about the boy's potential did not correspond to his performance. After a serious review of her various efforts to help this student handle his problem, she wondered if perhaps psychological conflict could be the source of the student's handicap in learning. But note the further steps that were taken before a referral was made. The sister had recourse to the chaplain and the principal, who in turn were baffled by the problem. It was at this point that psychiatric referral seemed advisable.

Hence, the most direct and helpful answer that can be given to the question, "When should I consider making a psychiatric referral?" is a simple rule of thumb which we both learned from Father Gerald Kelly, S.J.: "When the ordinary means of help at one's disposal are of no avail." Obviously, this rule must not become an excuse for quick referrals. The "ordinary means" rule implies that the teacher, for example, is sincerely facing the problem, doing her best to help the student, and is not trying to cover up "guilt" over her own lack of concern or failure. The "ordinary means" must be honestly and sincerely tried within the circumstances of each problem. Otherwise, the rule is robbed of its meaning and value.

Attempts to amplify this rule and to spell it out in greater detail are difficult and perhaps unnecessary. It is not easy to give an exhaustive list of "signs" to watch for in our students or parishioners. However, Father E. F. O'Doherty, a priest-psychologist who has written widely in this field, has suggested a rough guide to help discriminate the presence of illness that would seem to need psychiatric help. Though written in the context of spiritual direction and the confessional, the criteria given may be worth quoting for all our readers:

a) Morbid anxiety without a discernible cause, or anxiety out of all proportion to its apparent cause.

b) A painful or intolerable sadness ("depression") without reasonable cause.

c) Loss of normal adaptation, *e.g.*, a student who cannot study, a mother who cannot take an interest in her children, etc.

d) An inverse relation between an individual's expressed aims and the means he adopts to achieve them.

e) Over-eagerness to verbalize conscious ego-directed efforts to achieve levels of aspiration out of all proportion to actual levels of achievement.

f) Too much sheer physical involvement, *e.g.*, in prayer, or in overcoming temptation, especially of a reflex organic kind.

g) Psychosomatic disturbances—severe headaches, localized anaesthesias, paralyses, fainting, nausea, etc.

h) Any threat of suicide.[1]

The author concludes the list with this advice: "In these cases, the wise confessor and the wise spiritual director will temper the wind to the shorn lamb, and seek the natural aids and skills of the psychiatrist."

This leads us to our second question about how to make a referral. Already we have indicated the importance of channeling referrals through a person in an administrative position such as a principal, a dean, or a superior. This implies in turn that such people should know the mental-health resources of their community. Our sample interview between the school principal and Johnny's parents attempted to point up the psychological hurdles that have to be cleared in preparing for the referral. It is obvious that people who are in a position to make referrals should get to know the psychiatrists in their area. Religious superiors, spiritual fathers, and the like should be encouraged to make some acquaintance with those in the psychiatric professions.

Needless to say, their prime consideration in the choice of a psychiatrist should be his professional competence. There may be reasons for preferring a Catholic psychiatrist, but these should be clearly understood. As Dr. Philip R. Sullivan expresses it, in the conclusion of an excellent article called "The 'Psychiatric Catholic' ":

> A valid explanation is not to be found in the desire to utilize Catholicism as a psychiatric method, or in the fear that non-Catholic psychiatrists will lead Catholics astray, or in the direct application of theological truths to psychiatric therapy. An explanation must be sought, rather, in the cultural setting of the patient." [2]

Seemingly, a psychiatrist who is a Catholic may be in a better position to understand the religious cultural background of his Catholic patients, and it is no small aspect of therapy to have the patient feel comfortable and understood by the psychiatrist. But no one should assume that all Catholic psychiatrists are open to the full and important range of a patient's culture, nor that all non-Catholic psychiatrists lack such sensitivity.

But how does one really judge the competence of a psychiatrist? Most of us are not in a position to evaluate academic credentials, nor do we have available a handy "competency test." But we can, it seems, after several contacts know something of the psychiatrist's attitudes, and these can give us some help in judging whether or not we would feel assurance that he is the man to whom we can make referrals. A psychiatrist, Dr. Thomas Thale, spells this out in more detail:

> Catholics waste a lot of time worrying about Freud, when they could better be considering charity and integrity. The question is, will he [the psychiatrist] show true concern for the welfare of his patients? Does he protect them when they are helpless? Does he respect their confidences? Does he help them to grow and give them the opportunity to make their own decisions when they have more strength? It is up to your own perceptiveness to discern which ones are decisive and which merely hard-headed. You will also find a great deal of truth in a remark which I once picked up at a casual gathering, "There are all sorts of psychiatrists, but then there are all sorts of patients, too, and in time they frequently sort themselves out appropriately." Probably the internist, pastor, and chaplain can save a good deal of time and heartache for a patient if they help him to make an appropriate choice of a psychiatrist who is not only a good man, but a man who is good for them.[3]

This is sound advice. But if it should happen that one simply has not had the opportunity to get to know a psychiatrist and yet has the need for making a referral, he will have to rely on more general sources of information. What are some of these sources?

The American Psychiatric Association publishes each year a roster of its members which includes a geographical directory. This directory[4] also indicates whether the psychiatrist is in private practice and whether he is associated with a clinic or hospital. In addition it tells whether the psychiatrist is a diplomate of the American Board of Psychiatry and Neurology. If he is a diplomate, he has successfully completed specialty training in psychiatry and has passed the examinations required by this board.

Many cannot afford private psychiatric care. Hence, in making a referral it may be necessary to look for a publicly supported psychiatric clinic. Information about public mental-health clinics can be found in a directory published by the National Association for Mental Health.[5] It can be of great assistance in finding the nearest outpatient clinic to which one may refer.

Also, throughout the country there are social agencies which every day provide an enormous amount of help to a great number of people. These agencies are staffed with social workers, some particularly trained in psychiatric social work. The best of these agencies have a psychiatrist as a consultant available to them. Frequently these agencies may be used as an intermediate source of help. A person can be referred to such an agency, where the psychiatrist or medical social worker in turn can learn enough of the problem to help make plans for a further referral if this seems necessary. Hence, it will be well to be familiar with the social agencies nearby; a directory of member agencies is published annually by the Family Service Association of America.[6] Also, the National Conference of Catholic Charities publishes an annual directory of its member agencies.[7] And, in many communities there is a Council of Social Agencies or a Mental Health Information Service.

We are not implying that every priest and religious should forthwith send off for all these directories. But certainly they should be available to key personnel through whom many referrals are channeled. But we would like to repeat that there is no substitute for a personal acquaintance with the psychiatrists in one's area.

Once a referral has been made, of course, the referring person's contact with the patient does not necessarily come to an end. In this context there are a few questions that might be raised, especially by priests, when a student or penitent or parishioner is receiving psychiatric treatment.

The first has to do with the general question of how to deal with a person who is in psychiatric treatment. The general answer is this: ordinarily a priest should continue his priestly ministry to the psychiatric patient the same way as to anyone else, as far as his theological principles are concerned. He need not try to "adjust" these principles to the treatment, or compromise them in any way. As long as he acts within the scope of his vocational role as a priest and does not try to act as a supplementary therapist, there is little danger that his priestly ministry will be an obstacle to psychiatric treatment. However, there are examples where contact with a priest may, for a time, be medically inadvisable. The priest should try to understand and appreciate this himself, and also help the patient's family avoid a misunderstanding of the situation.

But the further question can arise, as indicated in one of the letters cited in the Introduction—the parishioner in treatment who comes to the priest with harsh criticisms of the psychiatrist, calling into question his ethics and his moral integrity. How should the priest handle this? Is the parishioner merely trying to play off the doctor against the priest? Is he showing his resistance to treatment by this type of criticism? Or is he reporting an objective fact?

Presumably, if the priest knows the psychiatrist in question and is sure of his competence, we would suggest that he gently and firmly persuade the patient to bring up these very feelings with the psychiatrist during the next treatment period. By thus bringing them into the treatment itself, the patient should be able to work through these difficulties and with the psychiatrist's help see them in their right perspective.

But what if there are grounds for suspecting that the treatment is really inept and harmful? If this were the suspicion in the area of physical medicine, a person could arrange for a medical consultation with another physician, who could, for example, corroborate the presence of cancer and approve the treatment or deny the same on the basis of his independent examination. But there are often too many intangibles in psychiatric treatment to make such a consultation feasible. Hence, given sufficient grounds for suspecting inept treatment, the priest's best course of action is to have the patient seek the advice of his family physician or some other doctor. A physician is usually in a better position than a priest to handle such a problem and can do so within the domain of his own profession.

We would like to note finally that we equate good psychiatry with good morality. We feel therefore that a competent psychiatrist would not find the Catholic Hospital Association's directive an impossible or unreal demand when it says:

> The psychiatrists and psychotherapists . . . must observe the cautions dictated by sound morality, such as: avoiding the error of pansexualism; never counselling even material sin; respecting the secrets that the patient is not permitted to reveal; avoiding the disproportionate risk of moral danger.[8]

We are not denying the existence of some knotty moral issues which psychiatric treatment raises, but well-trained psychiatrists should be able to respect the above directive with no hindrance to effective therapy. And if the psychiatrists themselves are in doubt about some of these issues, they can always consult experts in theology. For we hope that as the acquaintances increase between psychiatrists and religious personnel the consultations will become more of a two-way street.

8

Selection of the Religious Candidate

If I could wish for a longer life, it would be to see to it
that ever more prudence be used in choosing candidates
for the religious life.[1]

This could be a quotation from almost any religious
superior of our time. To demonstrate that the problem is
not a new one, and that centuries of time have not necessarily increased the "prudence used in choosing candidates
for the religious life," we chose this quotation from St.
Ignatius of Loyola.

The enormous growth of the number of psychological
tests and their use has been concurrent with the increased
popularity of psychiatry. This parallel growth in some ways
has been related and in other ways has been independent.
The reader will recall the letter quoted in our Introduction
in which a mother superior asks for the name of a psychological test that could be used in selecting women for the
religious life. The request is understandable.

Nearly everyone knows about aptitude tests, and it seems
that it should be possible to devise a test which could be
used to select people for their careers, or more specifically

one that could be given to candidates for the religious life that would tell whether they have the necessary aptitudes and whether they will "succeed" in that life. There are no such tests and it is not likely that there ever will be. But because there are frequent requests for such a test we felt it wise to include a chapter that attempts to tell something about psychological tests and their use. In this chapter we have relied heavily on our colleagues in clinical psychology.

In 1896 Lightner Witmer founded the first psychological clinic in the United States at the University of Pennsylvania. "Witmer's clinic, as the story goes, was the outgrowth of his response to the referral, by a nameless teacher, of the case of a bad speller." [2] The clinic grew as more referrals followed, and Witmer developed what would now be considered rudimentary tests. His stated aim has outlived his tests: "A psychological diagnosis is an interpretation of the observed behavior of human beings. Human psychology is an examination of man's spiritual nature. The unit of observation is a performance, but the unit of consideration is personality." [3]

Beginning with World War I, an attempt was made to use psychological tests for the selection of men for jobs. In this instance the job was that of being a soldier. The psychological tests used were intelligence tests. It was assumed that it took a certain degree of intelligence to survive as a soldier, and the tests were used to screen out those men who it was assumed were not "smart" enough to be soldiers. Some of this early testing aroused editorial alarm, since the tests were said to reveal that "half the population is below average in intelligence." But testing flourished and the term "I.Q." (intelligence quotient) entered into common parlance. In their excellent survey of clinical psychology Dr. Helen

Sargent and Dr. Martin Mayman have recently commented about the I.Q. in the history of psychological testing:

> The I.Q. has remained an important though often over-valued figure. It opened the doors of schools, hospitals, industries, and courts to psychologists who knew how to figure it, but sometimes indiscriminately closed the doors of institutions upon many persons whose scores fell, if by ever so little, below a certain ratio of chronological age expectancy to mental age. The sometimes tragic mis-use of intelligence tests has been at least balanced by their usefulness in understanding potentialities and limitations of the gifted and the defective.[4]

The present-day clinical psychologist may well use one of the standardized intelligence tests, but most of the tests he uses had a different origin. The insights gained by Freud about man encouraged first some physicians, and later many psychologists, to try to devise tests that would give a better picture of the inner psychological life of the individual patient. Most people have forgotten that it was Carl Jung who first began to work on a test of associations. The technique consisted of telling the patient a word, and asking the patient to respond with the first association that came to mind. Some of the words lacked emotional charge; others were specifically selected because they are often emotionally laden. The patient's response to the stimulus words allowed the psychiatrist to draw inferences about the patient's psychological functioning.

Another physician, Hermann Rorschach, was curious to learn how people tend to cope with a new situation. He wanted to develop a technique that could be standardized but would be new for every human being who was being studied. He finally devised the idea of using blots made by putting ink on a piece of paper. The subject being tested is confronted with a situation that is new to him. He is asked to tell the examiner what he sees in each of the ink blots. Rorschach and the many subsequent workers who have developed this test found that people tend to project themselves—that is, they use their ordinary ways of perceiving, feeling, and thinking as they respond to the request to tell what they see in the amorphous ink blot. The responses can be used by the psychologist to draw inferences about the patient's psychological functioning.

The Rorschach and other so-called projective tests (Thematic Apperception Test, Sentence Completion Test, and so on) all share one essential feature. They are designed to be "unstructured," so as to impose relatively little direction upon the subject's responses. There is in a strict sense no expected answer, no right or wrong answer. Using these tests the examiner picks up bits and fragments of a subject's passing associations—ideas which come to mind in response to such "open-ended" tasks as are put before him. Psychologists have found that these so-called "free" responses or "free" associations are in actuality not free at all but are prompted by secret preoccupations and enduring expectations. The responses are primed by wishes, fantasies, and fears, all of which can find expression in particular perceptual and behavioral biases and in certain warpings of the emotions and value systems of the individual.

But anyone who appreciates the subtlety, the enormous complexity, the often impenetrable intricacy and inscrutability of such unconscious processes will appreciate the fact that such techniques are of only limited usefulness in uncovering these central emotional dispositions of the personality. There is no quick, easy, well-paved and well-marked highway to the unconscious. Even the analysis of dreams, which according to Freud opened up a "royal road to the unconscious," is often bewildering or misleading, for dreams are opaque screens which may mask unconscious dispositions.

The Wechsler Adult Intelligence Scale is now commonly used by clinical psychologists. As the name implies, this test is designed to measure a person's global intelligence. It consists of eleven sub-tests, each of which is limited to a certain kind of question—general information, vocabulary, comprehension, similarities, object assembly, picture completion, and so on. An individual's performance on each sub-test, and on the test as a whole, can be compared with the standardization group made up of a representative sample of people in approximately the same age category as that of the person being tested. His score on any sub-test is converted into a standard score which represents his relative position in his particular age group. Thus, standard scores above ten represent better-than-average performance, and standard scores below ten represent below-average performance on any particular sub-test. The total of the sub-test scores also represents a relative position in the standardization group, and can be converted into an "I.Q. score" with the aid of a simple conversion table. The I.Q. score is only another way of indicating a person's relative position in his group when the total scores for the entire group are distributed from best to worst.

Another widely used type of test is the so-called paper-and-pencil test of personality functioning. All tests of this type share the same kind of structure. They generally consist of several hundred questions about a person's thoughts, feelings, and impulses which trouble him, or specific psychopathological symptoms he has at one time experienced or may now be experiencing. The subject is called upon to answer each question with a "yes," "no," or "question-mark" response. By far the most highly developed of these tests, and what may by now be the most widely used test in the United States, is the Minnesota Multiphasic Personality Inventory. This test differs from other such personality inventories largely in the nature of its standardization. Certain patterns of yes and no answers to special clusters of responses have been extracted statistically as being closely associated with certain types of illness or certain types of personality structure. A skilled clinical psychologist experienced in the use of this test can draw many useful inferences from a person's answers to the five hundred questions that comprise the test.

We wish to mention yet another test which has been very useful in vocational guidance—the Strong Vocational Interest Test. The test is misnamed because it does not in any sense "measure" vocational interests. Rather, it is standardized in such a way that it will reveal how congenially a person is likely to fit into one or another occupational group. The test consists of a variety of questions, such as, "Of these four men who are generally considered to be heroes, which one seems to you to be the greatest hero of the four?" The test includes questions not directly concerned with vocational interests—questions of opinion, value, judgment, aesthetic and social interests. The subject's answers to these questions are compared with the pattern of answers established through testing successful people in various vocational groups. Strong found that there is a discernible pattern in people's responses, so that those who are successful in a given vocation tend to think alike about many things, without ever having talked with one another about them. The pattern of interests of psychiatrists, for example, tends to be more similar to that of psychologists and social workers than to that of other medical specialists. Thus, this test can provide some hint as to the degree of "fit" that would be achieved by a person in a particular vocation.

Psychological tests are used in clinics to spot psychopathology, not to determine a person's vocational aptitudes. They may throw some light in a most general way upon the nature of the individual's capabilities, such as intelligence and intellectual curiosity. In addition, they tell something about the way in which the individual copes with his internal and external environments, and are helpful to the psychiatrist in prescribing treatment. Clinical tests are not designed to predict behavior. Psychologists tell us that they can learn how the patient is organized, what he is like psychologically, but they cannot predict his behavior in a given situation.

The above information, then, gives an initial answer to why a group of psychologists cannot provide us with a test that could be used to select religious candidates. In other words, psychologists tell us that it is impossible to anticipate the complicated qualifications that a person must have to succeed in a given career. Shortly after World War II, Dr. Lester Luborsky, Dr. Robert Holt, and others spent many years at The Menninger Foundation attempting to learn how to select young physicians who would "succeed" as psychiatrists.[5] With a large research grant and a great deal of professional talent, these researchers found that elaborate attempts at selection are hardly better than selection that is left to chance. They found what everyone knows—people who are grossly ill can usually be "selected out" with psychological tests. Thus, it is possible to avoid subjecting some people to rigorous professional training for which they are psychologically ill-fitted or which might actually increase the severity of their illness.

What, then, are we to say of the increasing tendency to obtain psychological test studies of young men and women who aspire to enter the seminary or the novitiate? The wish on the part of the novice masters and seminary directors for help along this line is understandable. A psychological test for those who aspire to the religious life so that one could predict success or failure would be of enormous help. But such a test does not exist. Yet the desire for it persists; as a result, attempts continue in the use of various psychological tests to screen out those who might fail, before they enter the religious life. The saving in time and human suffering and disappointment prods one again to look for the quick answer.

One can easily understand the wish for some certainty about selection; modern psychiatry and clinical psychology cannot contribute that certainty. While psychological tests are one of the most valuable aspects of present-day clinical diagnostic practice, they cannot be used to solve problems of selection. It is important to stress that their wholesale use in the elimination of candidates for the religious life is misguided. Their use as an *adjunct* to selection is warranted. But it is unlikely that a battery of psychological tests is as valuable a selection procedure as interviews with two or three experienced members of a religious community. The interviews plus the tests are at present a practice in some orders.

In the history of the growth and use of psychological tests, perhaps it was the *prognostic* hope that led many off to false trails. If the wiser heads prevail as far as the use of tests for religious aspirants is concerned, the whole question of prognosis will drop from the picture. For such people are not concerned about predicting the success or failure of aspirants. Hence, they are not concerned either about devising particular tests that will reveal "religious aptitudes" and the like. Rather, in all prudence and humility they see their tests simply as a supplement to the traditional screening procedures that have grown up in the Church.

Father William C. Bier, S.J.,[6] has made an eminently sound presentation of the use of psychological tests. He points out that it is really not valid to look to the series of trials and probations *within* the religious order or group as being an adequate procedure for selection. This is a misunderstanding of the purpose of the novitiate period and the subsequent training periods prior to final vows. These are not established primarily as sifting periods. Rather, it is presumed that, once a person has entered the religious life, having been judged *suitable* (it is in this assessment that the tests could make a contribution) and having chosen this life, the novitiate and subsequent training periods have as their primary aim the religious formation of the subject. True, it also serves as a sifting and testing period; but the subject's approach is not simply, "I'll give this a try"—that decision has already been made—but, rather, "I will live this life to the full and be formed and educated according to the rule of this order or congregation."

Father Bier is of the opinion that to err on the side of strictness and exclude doubtful cases seems the wiser path. Why? For several reasons: because of the difficulties of readjustment for those who leave; because of the good of the order, whose main efforts at this time are education and training, not therapy; and because of the increasing pressures resulting from delay, which make dismissal more and more difficult. A sound and sober testing program in the hands of a well-trained psychologist used in conjunction with the wisdom and experience of members of the order would be a step in the direction of the prudence mentioned by St. Ignatius.

In summary, then, psychological tests are not meant to supplant the traditional admission procedures. Nor are they aimed at discovering vocational aptitudes; rather, they aim at helping the examiners evaluate the psychological maturity and mental health of the applicants. Hence, their aim is quite modest, and as long as one recognizes the limitations of these tests they can serve a definite helpful function. In the balanced picture the psychologist and psychiatrist are seen as counselors to the superior, who must make the final decision concerning each applicant.

This last point is of paramount importance. The religious superior should not expect the psychiatrist or psychologist to give a judgment about a candidate's fitness for the religious life. This judgment can be made only by the religious superior. The psychiatrist must restrict his judgment to the medical field, the psychologist to the assessment of personality type and disorder. These judgments, in turn, may help the superior reach his decision. In any event, a psychiatrist's views on neurotic tendencies, on certain psychic weaknesses, and the like, in a particular candidate should not mean an automatic rejection. Just as we find some great figures of history who have overcome physical handicaps, so too should we expect to find many who have overcome psychic handicaps. It is uncertain how an Ignatius of Loyola or a Francis of Assisi would have shown up on the Rorschach or the Wechsler.

What, after all, is psychopathology? Psychiatric clinicians assume that anybody with signs of mental illness is sick. But that is only because people come presenting themselves as sick, asking about the nature of their sickness, and seeking help for it. In a nonclinical setting the same psychopathology may be irrelevant. Nearly everyone has some degree of sickness, and many learn to live with it. The question confronting the selectors of religious candidates is whether this pathology is likely to be so disruptive that the candidate will not be able to live the religious life successfully. At this point in time psychiatry is very limited in its ability to state categorically on the basis of knowledge of an individual's psychopathology whether he will be able to succeed in a given career. And it is certainly possible and quite realistic to see that the religious life can help a person compensate for particular psychic weaknesses. We must be open to this fact, while at the same time we are aware that the religious community is not meant to be a therapeutic one. But it can be such, without any disruption to the religious life.

Further research is obviously necessary before the prudence desired by St. Ignatius in the selection of religious candidates can be achieved. Such prudence will be hastened if magical expectations can be removed from the use of psychological tests to provide direct answers to questions about selection. Research programs designed to find the important questions to ask are at present more urgently needed than research selection programs set up specifically around psychological tests. What *are* the relevant questions to ask when attempting to select a religious candidate? And what quality of predictions can one make even without psychological tests about a candidate's success in the religious life? Such predictions can later be checked against the candidate's performance.

If the clinical psychologist is asked to help with selection he will want to know what one means by a "good candidate." And the more one looks at the question, "Who is a good candidate?" the more difficult the question becomes. Those responsible for selection need to attempt to make explicit for themselves what they believe the characteristics of a "good candidate" are, and what additional information they need to sharpen their ability to identify one.

The clinical psychologists who have been our advisers for this chapter tell us that selectors of religious candidates who use the above approach may find that they do not need psychological tests at all. The answers may be available in the applicant's life story and the impressions about the candidate gained by experienced religious. But before the data available can provide the answers, the right questions have to be identified.

9

The Psychiatrist and the Novice

It is a moot question whether there is more mental illness today than before or simply clearer recognition of the problem. As one observer of the American scene, Erik H. Erikson, has noted, "Our improved methods of detection and our missionary zeal expand together as we become aware of the problem, so that it would be hard to say whether today this country has bigger and better neuroses, or bigger and better ways of spotlighting them—or both." [1] In any event, as a result of public education and a recognition that early treatment means better and more successful treatment, our experience indicates that more and more religious superiors, seminary rectors, masters of novices, and the like, do attempt to provide early psychiatric care as needed for the people in their charge.

As an aside here, let us explain the last word in our chapter heading. For brevity's sake we chose one word, but it does not cover the people we have in mind. We do not limit our remarks to the "novice" in the technical sense of Canon Law—namely, the young religious who has been accepted into the initial training period of a religious order, wears a distinctive garb, but as yet has made no commitment of vows. Rather, we use the term in its generic sense, embracing all those who are at any stage of their professional religious training, whether in a religious house of formation or a diocesan seminary.

It is gratifying that many of the people who have charge of these trainees—"novices" in our use of the term—recognize the importance of early psychiatric help. For example, in one religious community known to us, any member may consult a psychiatrist simply by letting the superior know of his wish to do so. Such a policy helps prevent the dangerous progression of illness by making early treatment available.

Not all father rectors or mother superiors, however, are so convinced of the value of psychiatry. A negative attitude is often the result of some unfortunate past experience with a psychiatrist or of some unrealistic expectations of psychiatry. Admittedly, bad experiences can happen. As we have seen, there are not enough mental-health specialists, nor have all the available ones had good training. For example, a certain bishop who has "had his fill" of psychiatry actively discourages his priests from seeking psychiatric help. This bishop is an earnest, sincere shepherd of his flock. But in his early years a psychiatrist advised one of his priests to leave the priesthood and marry. Understandably, the bishop began to look at psychiatry with a jaundiced eye. Nor does it help to say that an adequately trained psychiatrist would not give such advice. One example of bad psychiatry booms loudly enough to drown out all other sounds of reason and intelligence. Yet reason and intelligence would suggest that one cultivate the same critical and judicious attitude in his thinking about psychiatry as he would in assessing competence in any other profession. A pervasive anti-psychiatry attitude helps no one.

A negative attitude may also result from one's false expectations of psychiatry. A superior referred a priest who had a problem of alcoholism, which is a severe form of illness and is often extremely difficult to treat. In spite of earnest efforts, the psychiatrist failed to cure the priest's drinking problem. The superior's disappointment at this was understandable, but it hardly warrants the generalization that psychiatry is never helpful.

Even if superiors are convinced of the value of psychiatry and of the importance of early treatment, such help may not be readily available. Increasing and better facilities will come, we hope, but at present there are some "psychiatric deserts" in the United States—areas without psychiatric clinics within a reasonable distance. This is a lack to be reckoned with, but all we can do now is deplore it.

Supposing help were available and the superiors were disposed to use it, what difficulties might arise? Some examples might illustrate the similarities and dissimilarities in a superior's dealing with illness of body and mind, and some of the problems that may be involved. The health of his community, of course, is but one of the many responsibilities of a superior, and in the event of sickness the customary procedure is to obtain proper medical help. The need for early treatment is obvious in the case of a physical affliction. Suppose, for example, that a "novice" develops acute abdominal discomfort. The pain progresses, becomes more severe and more localized. The physician is summoned. He examines the patient and orders laboratory tests. He then reports to the patient and to his superior that this is a case of acute appendicitis. Surgery is the treatment of choice, a treatment which must be done promptly to prevent serious complications. Everything is straightforward and obvious. The symptoms were apparent; because of his physical distress the novice reported to the superior; the superior could "see" the illness; the physician was called, the diagnosis made, and the necessary treatment undertaken.

Assume a more serious state of affairs. Let us say that a seminarian for unexplainable reasons is losing weight, has an unusual sense of chronic fatigue, and has just developed a cough productive of sputum. The superior is informed, a physician called, a diagnosis made. The results indicate that the seminarian has pulmonary tuberculosis. The physician may well report his findings to the superior before reporting them to his patient. He may even ask the superior to be present when he tells the seminarian of the disease. For, in the light of the nature and length of the treatment required, ordination will have to be deferred. All concerned know the facts and their implications.

Compare the foregoing medical situations with yet another, this time a psychiatric illness. A scholastic goes to his superior and expresses the desire to consult a psychiatrist, or is sent to a psychiatrist on the advice of someone else. Let us assume that after the initial examinations the psychiatrist recommends psychotherapy and starts treating the patient. To help arrive at an understanding of the illness, the psychiatrist will obtain from the patient a story of his life, together with details of his present illness. Such information is necessarily quite personal and highly confidential; if it is not, it is not complete, and the psychiatrist cannot have an understanding of the patient. For, as we have noted earlier, there is something in the very nature of emotional illness and the dynamics of personality that involves the psychiatrist in the inner psychic life of the patient. Frequently this may include matters of conscience which the patient is willing to unfold to the doctor because he knows this is a condition for his being helped. And he feels free thus to lay bare his inner personal life because he knows his communication is "privileged"—that is, that the psychiatrist has the professional obligation not to divulge this confidential information to anyone else without the patient's permission.

Let us assume that the treatment goes well between the doctor and his patient. However, at the seminary the superior is becoming somewhat anxious. Apart from knowing that one of his community is receiving psychotherapy, he is in the dark. The only visible "progress report" is the monthly bill from the doctor. The superior wishes to know what is going on, yet he does not wish to interfere with the treatment. What should be the nature of his relationship with the psychiatrist? The situation is obviously different from the prior examples of the physician treating the patient with appendicitis or the one with tuberculosis.

We touch here upon an area that can be complicated and delicate. It is an area also where possible misunderstandings, on the part of the psychiatrist, the patient, and the religious superior, may further confuse the issue.

The primary obligation of the psychiatrist is *to his patient*, and naturally he is concerned about anything that may interfere with the patient's chance of recovery. The superior's obligation is twofold: to the individual and to the religious community. The question then is this: If one of the superior's subjects is receiving psychiatric treatment, is there necessarily a conflict between the physician's, the patient's, and the superior's obligations?

Let us approach this question in a rather roundabout way. First, the Church has always been careful to protect the rights of conscience of her members. The Church is justly concerned also about the proper formation of conscience, knowing that the individual's immediate norm of conduct is his conscience. But one's moral conscience is just part of his interior psychic life which, as Father John C. Ford, S.J., writes, includes also "the consciousness of one's own thoughts good and bad, one's own emotional tendencies, instincts and dispositions good and bad, conscious and un-conscious, and the memory of one's own secret deeds good and bad." [2] Each individual has an inviolable right to protect his interior psychic life, the content of which he alone may guard or freely reveal. This right is as sacred as a person's right to his good name, to his possessions or to his bodily integrity. As Pope Pius XII pointed out in his "Allocution on Applied Psychology," [3] it is as immoral to enter into the domain of one's inner psychic life against his will as it is to steal his goods or do physical harm.

This whole area of one's inner psychic life is spoken of technically as the "internal forum." What one person reveals to another in the internal forum—that is, this area of the inner psychic life—is sacrosanct. Within the confines of the sacrament of Penance, this sacrosanctness is absolute; the "seal of confession" admits no exceptions. A glance at any textbook on moral theology will reveal how carefully this confessional secrecy is hedged round with many safeguards. Even when a person outside of confession reveals something of his inner psychic life—matters of conscience, for ex-ample—for the sake of getting counsel and spiritual direc-tion, this matter remains in the internal forum and obliges the spiritual director to professional secrecy. It is a privileged communication, and the spiritual director can use the knowledge only in his relationship with the other party. A particular aspect of the internal forum pertains to the superior's dealing with the individual members of his community in his role as head and "father" of the community. In this instance the term "paternal forum" is sometimes used.

The internal forum is distinguished from the "external forum," which pertains to the order of government and administration, primarily from the point of view of the public and common good. It is a juridical term, and is ordinarily used in the context of the government of a religious order or congregation. For example, a religious superior acts in the external forum when he sends Father X to another parish. The superior acts in the external forum when he publicly rebukes Father Y for maliciously setting fire to the schoolhouse. When the superior approves of Brother Z's Fulbright scholarship that will take him to Germany for a year's postgraduate study, he acts in the external forum.

In summary, we can say that when a superior is acting *principally* in the interests of the individual, he is acting in the internal and paternal forum; when acting *principally* in the public interest of his community, he is acting in the external forum.[4]

While these two forums are clearly distinguished in principle, their interrelationship can cause practical difficulties and raise problems. Because of the sacrosanct character of the internal forum, a superior may not use knowledge of it in the external forum without the subject's approval. For example, if a subject freely reveals to the superior (as to a father) that he is an alcoholic, the superior cannot publicly punish him, or on the basis of that knowledge alone send him off to some out-of-the-way mission.

As head of the religious community, however, the superior's actions are not restricted solely, or even predominantly, to the external forum. In the centuries-old tradition of Christian spirituality, religious have always been exhorted and encouraged to be completely open with superiors. Government of religious orders is expected to be paternal, not juridical and penal. Yet this does not mean that there is no set of rules and regulations that pertain to external government. There is a balance to be maintained. Canon Law (Canon 530) forbids superiors to *exact* a manifestation of conscience from their subjects. Father Adam C. Ellis, S.J., has written a brief and clear explanation of this Canon.[5] It recognizes the possible difficulties that could arise if the superior began to cross back and forth between the two forums. Still, such manifestation of conscience, while it cannot be exacted, is certainly encouraged. Without it, paternal government becomes merely an empty phrase. The rules and constitutions of all orders and congregations emphasize the paternal relationship between subjects and superiors, and those who vow to live the religious life assume the obligation to make such paternal government a reality. What we have said about religious applies, *mutatis mutandis*, to the relationship of diocesan priests with their bishop.

The psychiatrist who is asked to examine a young religious or to treat one should realize that this patient is in something of a unique position. He has given up some rights, and the psychiatrist needs to be cognizant of this. As a member of a religious community, the patient stands in a special relationship to the superior; this is not an exact replica of the father-son relationship in all its details, but it is very much like it in spirit. The religious has freely sacrificed something of his independence and autonomy. While the psychiatrist's primary responsibility is always to the patient, he automatically assumes a secondary responsibility to the superior and to the order. The physician's relationship with the superior which results from his twofold responsibility—to the patient and to the order—pertains to the paternal forum. Hence, any communication between the psychiatrist and the superior shares the confidential privilege of the paternal forum. Thus, what the psychiatrist reveals may not be used by the superior in the external forum. If necessary, the religious patient should be reminded, both for his own good and for the good of the treatment, of his special situation as a member of an order. The openness between doctor and superior, however, must not involve the revelation of anything that pertains to the forum of conscience—this the superior himself must recognize as an area he cannot force. But surely the doctor should not be sealed off from the superior so that their only point of contact is in the payment for services rendered.

Clinical experience leads us to distinguish two general categories of situations which make the interchange between psychiatrist and superior relatively simple on the one hand and quite complicated on the other. The distinction rests somewhat on the nature of the illness presented, and also on the nature of the existing relationship of the patient and the superior. The simple category falls in an area where there are no moral problems mixed up with the mental or emotional disturbance; at the same time there is a good relationship between superior and subject so that the patient finds no difficulty eventually in having the whole problem clarified for the superior. The complicated category involves a moral problem and a poor relationship between superior and subject, marked by a fear that the superior might take action in the external forum were he to know of the subject's problem. Clinical examples of each category may help clarify this distinction, from which we may be able to draw some guiding principles.

Sister Angela, a young nun not yet professed of final vows, had been teaching for two years in an elementary school. Her mother superior sought a psychiatric examination for her because of episodes of depression that made her life miserable. Ordinary help had been of no avail. The early interviews with the doctor revealed that the sister had always compared herself with others, with most unkind results. The feeling of falling short in everything was persistent. In the novitiate she managed the problem well enough amid the busy but externally trivial round of duties. But, precipitated into the busy life of teaching, she was less successful at coping with her problems. Though she had a very difficult group of fifth-grade youngsters, she felt that anyone else could do a far better job. Convinced that her students were learning less and that discipline in her class was the worst in the school, she began to feel more and more that she was not even a good nun. Amid the litany of self-criticism that she presented to the psychiatrist, she admitted that she had shed many tears over this, and because of her many "failures" was withdrawing more and more into herself. Her extreme moodiness prompted her superior to seek this evaluation.

To the psychiatrist this was a common form of neurotic depression. When he suggested psychotherapy twice a week,

Sister Angela insisted that this would not help and, besides, she did not deserve such special treatment. She had really hoped that the psychiatrist would prescribe some medicine that would solve her problem—pills twice a day were simpler than "talking therapy" twice a week. Part of the doctor's task was to help the sister accept treatment and to help her approach the mother superior about her need for it.

As the therapy progressed, the parties involved—Mother Superior, Sister Angela, and the psychiatrist—sat down together and freely talked over the problem and the progress that was being made. Sister Angela had always been open with her superiors; however, with this particular problem, she had so little understanding of it herself that she had been quite helpless to explain it. Further, there was no moral problem involved, and Sister Angela saw no threat in the situation. The treatment was short-termed, and Sister Angela emerged with a greater facility for self-acceptance and a clearer grasp of her own identity as a nun.

Contrast this with a second clinical example:

Mr. Kelly, a seminarian pursuing his theological studies preparatory for the priesthood, came to the psychiatrist. One of his classmates suggested this source of help to his puzzled superior, who seemingly could not "get through" to the troubled Mr. Kelly.

In the first session with the psychiatrist, Mr. Kelly spoke vaguely about being unhappy, but the doctor sensed some deeper problem. The vagueness persisted. At the second session the seminarian said he felt psychiatry could not really help him and regretted having come in the first place. The doctor said he could not help unless Mr. Kelly could bring himself to explain what was troubling him. As the doctor worked at and succeeded in gaining the patient's trust, Mr. Kelly finally blurted out that he had not made a good confession in three years. As long as he could remember, he said, he had been sexually attracted to men rather than women; in this regard there had been both thoughts and actions which were never confessed. As the psychiatrist learned more about these abnormal sexual interests, he pointed out to the patient that a long period of treatment might be necessary to give him the needed help.

To initiate prolonged treatment, Mr. Kelly needed his superior's permission. However, he had hidden his problem so long that he felt it would be impossible to talk to his superior about it. Besides, he did not want to leave the seminary or compromise his position as a candidate for Holy Orders. To become a priest was still his goal. The seminarian therefore reported to the superior only that the doctor had suggested the need for extended treatment. Permission was granted and the psychotherapy began.

In such circumstances what is the relationship between the psychiatrist and the superior? Obviously the psychiatrist cannot communicate the conscience matter of the patient, nor would the superior expect it. But the patient may well view *any* communication with the superior as a threat. What is to be the psychiatrist's attitude toward this?

While the psychiatrist's first duty is to act in the best interests of the patient, this can also be in the best interest of everyone concerned, including the patient's superior. The doctor must approach the patient in his unique status as a member of a religious order, as one, therefore, who has made a contract prior to seeing a psychiatrist. When the patient joined his order, he knew this included his having a religious superior to whom he had certain obligations not abrogated by the new relationship with the psychiatrist. In other words, though a psychiatric patient, he still has obligations to his order, one of which is to inform his superior of the state of his health, so that he can be properly directed and governed.

We wish to correct the misconception that most psychiatric patients are fragile beings who have to be specially protected. The patient comes to the psychiatrist with certain problems. These are his problems, they belong to him, and in the last analysis he has to assume full responsibility for them. Hence, it is not for the psychiatrist to judge a patient's fitness for receiving Holy Orders or taking vows—this is clearly beyond the psychiatrist's professional competence. But it is his job to insist that the patient recognize his own responsibilities. If the patient does not recognize them, the psychiatrist obviously has work to do.

Let us consider this from the superior's point of view. If he sends one of his subjects to a psychiatrist, he wants eventually to get some report. He cannot otherwise provide effectively for his subject. If adequate information is not forthcoming from the patient himself, and if an important step such as ordination is at issue, the superior needs vital information. He should not ask the psychiatrist, "Should this man be ordained?" but rather, "What is the state of this man's mental health? Is he capable of making a decision that involves profound responsibilities? Is he healthy enough to assume new obligations?" Such questions the psychiatrist can answer without detriment to the therapy and without revealing matters of the internal forum. The superior's questions should be clearly framed, so that the doctor in turn will have some assurance that his report will be correctly understood.

Hence, in the case of Mr. Kelly, the doctor, having obtained the patient's permission, could report to the superior about the nature of the patient's mental health. If the patient does not respond to treatment, the doctor should persuade the patient himself to reveal his difficulty to his superior in the paternal forum. Of course, the religious can refuse and thus tie the psychiatrist's hands the same way he could a spiritual father's or confessor's. Like the others, the psychiatrist can do nothing beyond warning the subject of his serious obligation. The psychiatrist cannot violate his professional obligation of secrecy by revealing to the superior the patient's moral problem.

Because there are cases in which a moral problem is involved, a problem which is not revealed to the superior, Father Ford suggests a rule of thumb as a practical norm for protecting both the superior and the order—admit no one to final vows or to Holy Orders until a year has elapsed after termination of psychiatric treatment.[6] This rule could forestall many a difficult situation. If adopted, it should be made known to subjects—not to discourage getting treatment, but to encourage successful termination of treatment. But, as Father Ford cautions, this rule of thumb "seems to presuppose that a need of psychiatric care creates a presumption of disqualifying mental illness, or of clear unsuitability for orders." To undercut this type of presumption, which can frequently be misleading, the rule should not be applied in a rigid manner. At the same time, however, the burden of proof against the presumption implied by the rule should be the religious subject's responsibility. "If a subject," writes Father Ford, "who has been permitted to undergo psychotherapy is unwilling to furnish by himself or through the psychiatrist adequate information on these points, he obviously courts an unfavorable decision on his ordination."

Besides the difficult area of confidentiality, there is another problem raised concerning "the psychiatrist and the novice." How should a busy superior, for example, handle requests of subjects who ask permission to see a psychiatrist? Is the mere asking in itself a sufficient reason for granting the request? Or is there a danger that such requests will become a fad? We doubt that such a danger exists. But the superior has the right to make sure that his subject has availed himself of the ordinary means of help—the help of his father confessor or spiritual director. Given that assurance, the superior may reasonably grant the subject's request.

Undoubtedly other problem areas exist; neither this final chapter nor the book itself is meant to be an exhaustive treatment of "psychiatry and religious faith." There are problems that are specific and unique to the various stages of the professional training of priests and nuns. The psychological and sociological dimensions of career preparation are being studied.[7] The initial adjustment to religious life, the passage from novitiate to studies, the passage from temporary vows to final vows, the tensions surrounding a step as decisive as ordination to the priesthood—all these are critical events in the life of the religious.[8] The superior's desire to help his subject adjust to these transitions is part of his concern about the mental health of his religious community.

Postscript

At this point we end our present effort to tell something about mental illness, psychiatry, and a few selected problem areas through which mental illness and psychiatry enter the lives of religious men and women. Let us note once more that, while priests and nuns were envisioned as our primary reading public, we feel this book addresses itself to the Catholic laity as well. At best, however, this book can be only a primer, and we hope it will encourage the reader to further study.

We hope that we have succeeded in conveying our conception of an enlightened attitude toward the mentally ill and the mental-health professions. Admittedly this conception is based on an ideal that is still far from realization. Many today, when confronted with the fact of serious mental illness in a loved one, turn for help and meet nothing but disappointment and frustration. Adequate facilities for treatment may not be available within their geographical or financial range. Still, the ideal we have presented is not impossible. The cries of the mentally ill are compelling. The cries for concerted action to prevent mental illness and to treat it when prevention fails are equally compelling. However idealistic we may seem in this brief book, we hope our efforts relate something of the science and art of psychiatry to all who are religiously dedicated to the service of God's struggling creatures. The mysteries of our Christian faith all point to the primacy of love—a love of God which in our exile on earth must manifest itself in our love of our fellow men. To paraphrase St. John, we cannot profess to love the hidden God if we fail to love every person who enters our lives. This love of God in his creatures admits no arbitrary selections. Our love of our fellow men becomes a mockery if we make choices on the basis of color, creed, political affiliation, or even the presence or absence of mental health.

The world of man is ever approaching a greater and greater unity, amid an expanding complexity—a world of which Teilhard de Chardin could say, "The day is not far distant when humanity will realize that biologically it is faced with a choice between suicide and adoration." [1] We can face that world with the Christian hope that Pope John XXIII endeavored so heroically to instill in us. For our late Holy Father appealed to all men to cultivate those attitudes which unite and to abandon those which divide. His prayer was ever that God may "enkindle the wills of all, so that they may overcome the barriers that divide, cherish the bonds of mutual charity, understand others, and pardon those who have done them wrong. By virtue of His action, may all peoples of the earth become as brothers, and may the most longed-for peace blossom forth and reign always between them." [2]

In this spirit—and we trust that this book was conceived in this spirit—there is a clear need today, not for nonsensical competition between religion and the mental-health professions, but for intelligent and informed cooperation. The individual contribution each of us makes in the area of mental health will not be statistically measurable. But the contribution must be made. Occasionally perhaps such a contribution will have about it a glow of splendor. In that case, we might fittingly quote the words that playwright Robert Bolt put on the lips of St. Thomas More: "No doubt it delights God to see splendor where He only looked for complexity." [3]

Reference Notes

Chapter 1. Psychiatry and Religion

1. William C. Menninger. *Psychiatry in a Troubled World.* New York: Macmillan, 1948.
2. Clemens E. Benda. In: *Some Considerations of Early Attempts in Cooperation between Religion and Psychiatry.* New York: Group for the Advancement of Psychiatry Symposium No. 5, 1958.
3. Karl Menninger. "Psychiatry Looks at Religion." In: *A Psychiatrist's World: The Selected Papers of Karl Menninger, M.D.,* B. H. Hall, ed. New York: Viking, 1959.
4. Wolfgang Goethe. *Goethes Werke,* Volume 3. Leipzig and Vienna: Bibliographisches Institut.
5. Gerald Kelly, S.J. Personal communication.
6. Rudolf Allers. "Psychiatry and the Role of Personal Belief." In: *Faith, Reason and Modern Psychiatry,* Francis J. Braceland, ed. New York: P. J. Kenedy, 1955.
7. Andrew M. Greeley. *Strangers in the House: Catholic Youth in America.* New York: Sheed and Ward, 1961.
8. Alfred Delp. *The Prison Meditations of Father Alfred Delp.* New York: Herder and Herder, 1963.
9. John L. Thomas. *Religion and the American People.* Westminster, Maryland: Newman Press, 1963.
10. Pope John XXIII. *Pacem in Terris* (Encyclical, April 1963).

Chapter 2. The Mental-Health Problem

1. John F. Kennedy. "Message from the President of the United States Relative to Mental Illness and Mental Retardation." U.S. House of Representatives, Document No. 58, February 5, 1963.
2. Clifford A. Beers. *A Mind That Found Itself.* New York: Longmans, Green, 1907.
3. "1963 Fact Sheet—Facts about Mental Illness." New York: National Association for Mental Health, 1963.
4. National Council on Alcoholism. Statistics, 1961.
5. *Medicolegal Digest,* editorial, 1:6, September 1960.
6. U.S.P.H.S. "Toward Quality in Nursing—Needs and Goals." Report of the Surgeon General's Consultant Group on Nursing. Publication No. 992. Washington: U.S. Government Printing Office, 1963.
7. Joseph H. Fichter. *Southern Parish.* Chicago: University of Chicago Press, 1951.
   ———. *Social Relations in the Urban Parish.* Chicago: University of Chicago Press, 1954.
   Andrew M. Greeley. *The Church and the Suburbs.* New York: Sheed and Ward, 1959.
   Joseph B. Schuyler. *Northern Parish.* Chicago: Loyola University Press, 1960.
8. Karl Menninger. "Take Your Choice." In: *A Psychiatrist's World,* op. cit.
9. Albert Deutsch. *The Shame of the States.* New York: Harcourt, Brace, 1948.
10. Pat Johnson. *Topeka State Journal,* February 25, 1955.
11. Pierre Teilhard de Chardin. *Letters from a Traveller.* New York: Harper, 1962.
12. Pearl S. Buck. *The Child Who Never Grew.* New York: John Day, 1950.

Chapter 3. The Meaning of Mental Illness

1. Pope John XXIII. Op. cit.
2. Karl Menninger, et al. *The Vital Balance.* New York: Viking, 1963.
3. Stanley H. King. *Perceptions of Illness and Medical Practice.* New York: Russell Sage Foundation, 1962.

4. Harvey Graham. *The Story of Surgery*. New York: Doubleday, 1939.

5. Richard Hunter and Ida MacAlpine. *Three Hundred Years of Psychiatry, 1535-1860*. London: Oxford University Press, 1963.

6. Ibid.

7. George Hagmaier, C.S.P. and Robert Gleason, S.J. *Counselling the Catholic*. New York: Sheed and Ward, 1959.

8. Karl Menninger. "Communication and Mental Health." *Menninger Quarterly*, 16:1-5, Winter 1962.

9. Marie Jahoda. *Current Concepts of Positive Mental Health*. New York: Basic Books, 1958.

10. Alfred Delp. Op. cit.

11. Marie Jahoda. Op. cit.

12. Ibid.

13. John C. Ford, S.J. *Religious Superiors, Subjects and Psychiatrists*. Westminster, Maryland: Newman Press, 1963.

Chapter 4. Dimensions of Psychiatric Theory

1. Earl D. Bond. *Thomas W. Salmon—Psychiatrist*. New York: W. W. Norton, 1950.

2. J. Sanbourne Bockoven. *Moral Treatment in American Psychiatry*, New York: Springer, 1963.

3. Ibid.

4. Frank L. Wright, Jr. *Out of Sight, Out of Mind*. Philadelphia: National Mental Health Foundation, 1947.

5. L. L. Whyte. *The Unconscious before Freud*. New York: Basic Books, 1960.

6. Alden L. Fisher. "Freud and the Image of Man." *Proceedings of the American Catholic Philosophical Association*, 35:45-77, 1961.

7. Ibid.

8. For the implications of transference phenomenon in the pastoral relationship, see: Godin, André. "Transference in Pastoral Counselling." *Theology Digest*, 9:78-83, Spring 1961.

For the moral issues involved in transference and related aspects of psychiatric treatment, see the excellent chapter on "Psychiatry and Catholicism" in: John C. Ford and Gerald Kelly. *Contemporary Moral Theology*. Volume I. Westminster, Maryland: Newman Press, 1959.

9. Peter Flood, editor. *New Problems in Medical Ethics*. Vol. 2. Westminster, Maryland: Newman Press, 1956.

10. Alden L. Fisher. Op. cit.

11. Karl Menninger, Martin Mayman, and Paul W. Pruyser. *A Manual for Psychiatric Case Study*. New York: Grune and Stratton, 1962.
12. Alden L. Fisher. "Psychoanalysis and Religion." *Insight*, 1:27-36, Fall 1962.
13. Jerome S. Bruner. "Freud and the Image of Man." In: *Freud and the 20th Century*, Benjamin N. Nelson, ed. New York: Meridian Books, 1957.

Chapter 5. *Psychiatric Practice—Diagnosis and Treatment*

1. Bernard H. Hall. "Prescribing Hospitalization." *Bulletin of the Menninger Clinic*, 22:207-213, November 1958.
2. In: Frank L. Wright, Jr. Op. cit.

Chapter 6. *Psychiatric Practice—Psychotherapy*

1. Ernst Ticho. "Principles of Psychotherapy." Unpublished manu-manuscript.
2. Carl Epstein. "Psychotherapy at The Menninger Clinic." *Menninger Quarterly*, 13:1-6, Spring 1959.
3. Edward Bibring. "Psychoanalysis and the Dynamic Psychotherapies." *J. Am. Psa. Assn.*, 2:745-770, 1954.
4. Gerald Gurin, Joseph Veroff, and Sheila Feld. *Americans View Their Mental Health*. New York: Basic Books, 1960.

Chapter 7. *The Psychiatric Referral*

1. E. F. O'Doherty. "Psychoanalysis, Psychotherapy and Spiritual Direction." In: *The Priest and Mental Health*, E. F. O'Doherty and S. Desmond McGrath, eds. Staten Island: Alba House, 1963.
2. Philip R. Sullivan. "The 'Psychiatric Catholic.'" *America*, 108:199-201, February 9, 1963.
3. Thomas Thale. Unpublished manuscript.
4. *List of Fellows and Members of the American Psychiatric Association*. American Psychiatric Association, 1270 Avenue of the Americas, New York, N.Y. 10020.
5. "A Directory of Outpatient Psychiatric Clinics and Other Mental Health Resources in the United States and Territories." National

Association for Mental Health, 1790 Broadway, New York, N.Y.
10019.
6. Family Service Association of America, 192 Lexington Ave., New
York, N.Y.
7. National Conference of Catholic Charities, 1346 Connecticut Ave.,
N.W., Washington 6, D.C.
8. *Ethical and Religious Directives for Catholic Hospitals.* St. Louis:
Catholic Hospital Association, 1955.

Chapter 8. Selection of the Religious Candidate

1. St. Ignatius of Loyola.
2. Helen D. Sargent and Martin Mayman. "Clinical Psychology." In:
American Handbook of Psychiatry, Silvano Arieti, ed. New
York: Basic Books, 1959.
3. Ibid.
4. Ibid.
5. Robert R. Holt and Lester Luborsky. *Personality Patterns of
Psychiatrists.* Vol. I. New York: Basic Books, 1958.
6. William C. Bier, S.J. "Psychological Testing of Candidates and
the Theology of Vocation." *Review for Religious*, 12:291-304,
1953. "Practical Requirements of a Program for the Psychological Screening of Candidates." *Review for Religious*, 13:13-
27, 1954.

Chapter 9. The Psychiatrist and the Novice

1. Erik H. Erikson. *Childhood and Society.* New York: Norton, 1950.
2. John C. Ford, S.J. Op. cit.
3. Pope Pius XII. "Allocution on Applied Psychology." *The Catholic Mind*, 56:353-368, 1958.
4. John C. Ford, S.J. Op. cit.
5. Adam C. Ellis, S.J. "Superiors and Manifestation of Conscience."
Review for Religious, 2:101-108, 1943.
6. John C. Ford, S.J. Op. cit.
7. Thomas W. Klink. "The Career of Preparation for the Ministry."
Unpublished manuscript.
8. Joseph H. Fichter. *Religion as an Occupation.* South Bend, Indiana: Notre Dame Press, 1961.
Eli Ginzberg. *Occupational Choice.* New York: Columbia University Press, 1951.

Postscript

1. Pierre Teilhard de Chardin. Op. cit.
2. Pope John XXIII. Op. cit.
3. Robert Bolt. *A Man for All Seasons*. New York: Random House, 1960.

Index